17

20

1

10

MATH
MAZES
Times Tables

by Angelika Scudamore

22

4

18

6

25

13

14

ARCTURUS

ARCTURUS

This edition published in 2019 by Arcturus Publishing Limited
26/27 Bickels Yard, 151–153 Bermondsey Street,
London SE1 3HA

Edited by Sebastian Rydberg
Written by William Potter
Illustrated by Angelika Scudamore
Designed by Trudi Webb

ISBN: 978-1-78888-487-7
CH006622NT
Supplier 29, Date 0319, Print run 7813

Printed in China

How to Use This Book

Welcome to the "funtastic" world of times tables mazes!
This book is full of exciting mazes to help you learn the basics
of multiplication and division.

Locate the start of each maze,
and read the instructions to
help you solve it.

Solve each calculation, and
then choose the correct path
to reach the end.

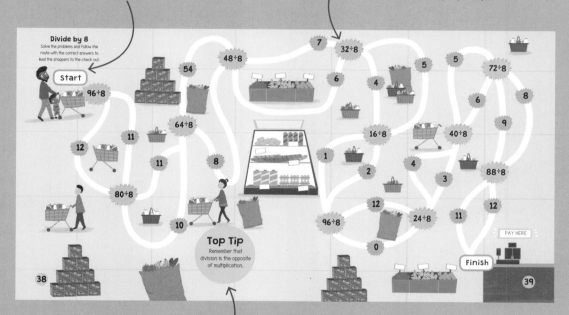

Divide by 8
Solve the problems and follow the route with the correct answers to lead the shoppers to the check out.

Start

96÷8

54

48÷8

7   32÷8

6

4

5   5   72÷8

6   8

9

64÷8

11

12

11

8

16÷8   40÷8

1

2   4   88÷8

3

80÷8

10

96÷8   12   24÷8   11   12

0

38

Top Tip
Remember that division is the opposite of multiplication.

PAY HERE

Finish   39

Some topics come with a
Top Tip to help you on
the way.

If you are stuck you can
always check the answers on
pages 89-96.

Doubles

Guide the fairy back to her toadstool home. Follow the problems that are doubles. Watch out for the gnomes!

Start

2+4

3+3

3+4

8+8

6+6

4+4

5+5

9+8

Top Tip

A double is where two numbers the same are added together.
Double 3 = 3 + 3

17+7

5+6

9+9

16+6

Finish

1+1

20+30

7+7

2+2

8+9

10+12

12+12

3+5

Multiples of 2

Lead the astronaut through the stardust back to the rocket. Follow the numbers that are multiples of 2.

Start

2

7

9

16

8

12

15

23

6

Top Tip

Multiples of 2 are numbers in the two times table. Multiples of 2 can be divided by 2.

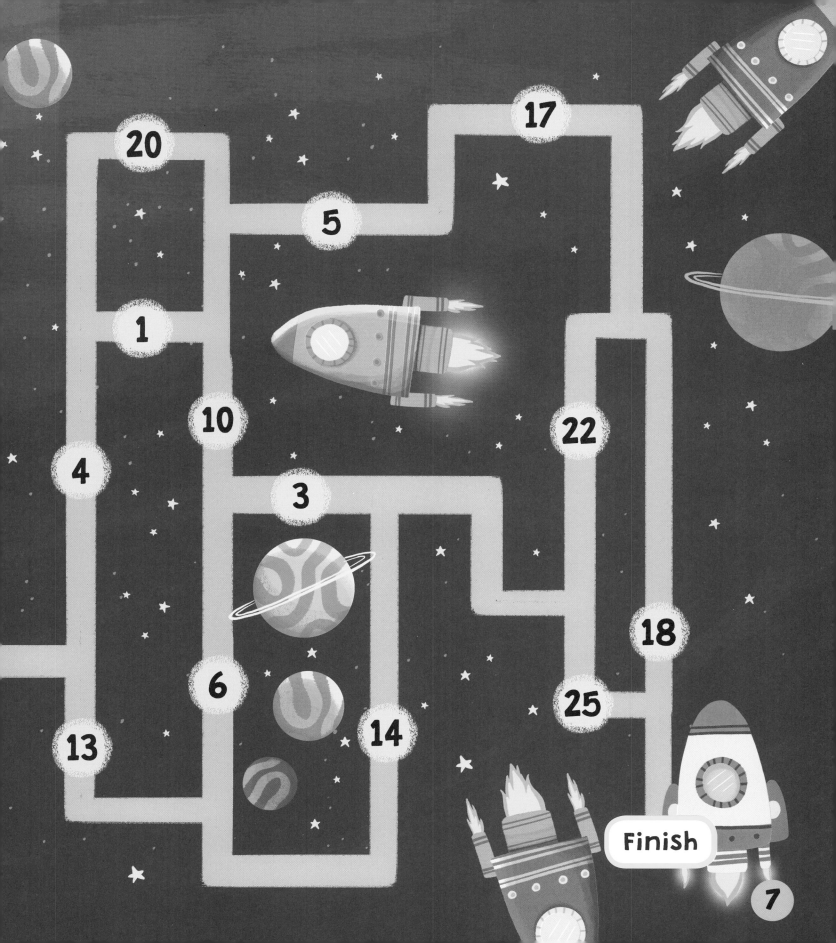

Multiples by 2

Help the girl to find her friend at the skate park.
Work out the calculations and follow
the correct answers.

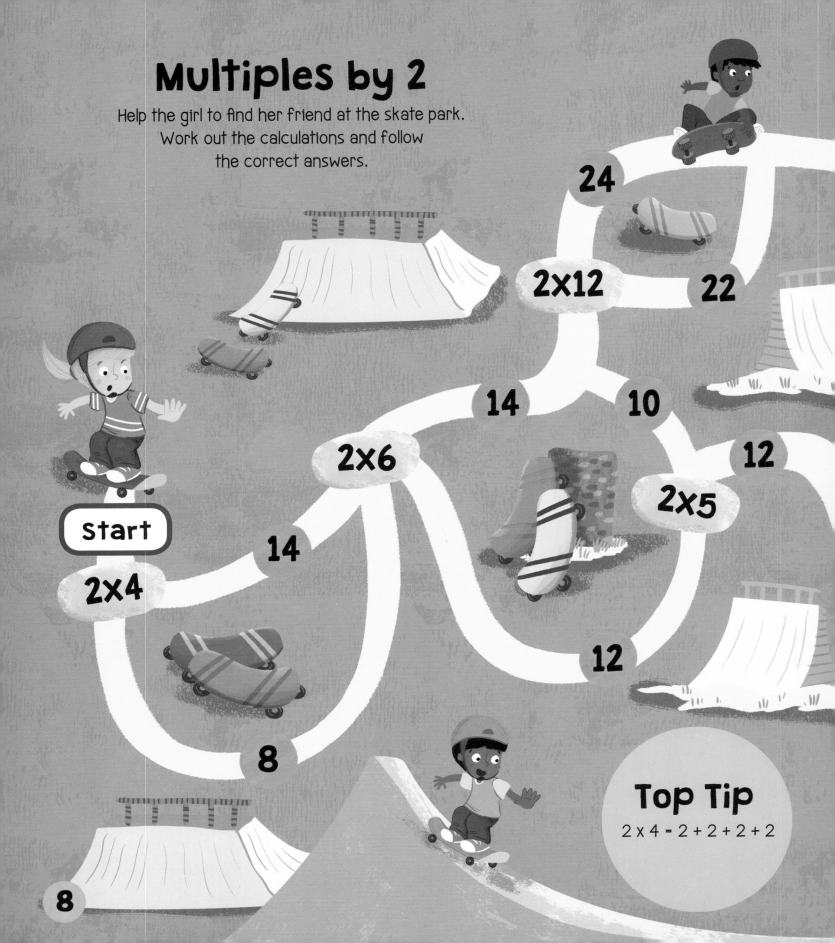

24

2X12

22

14

10

2X6

12

2X5

Start

14

2X4

12

8

8

Top Tip

2 x 4 = 2 + 2 + 2 + 2

2x2
3
4
2x7
2
14
2x1
2
1
18
2x8
2x10
16
2x9
20
21
19
18
Finish

9

Divide by 2

Can you guide the boy across the city in time to watch the movie? Work out the calculations and follow the correct answers.

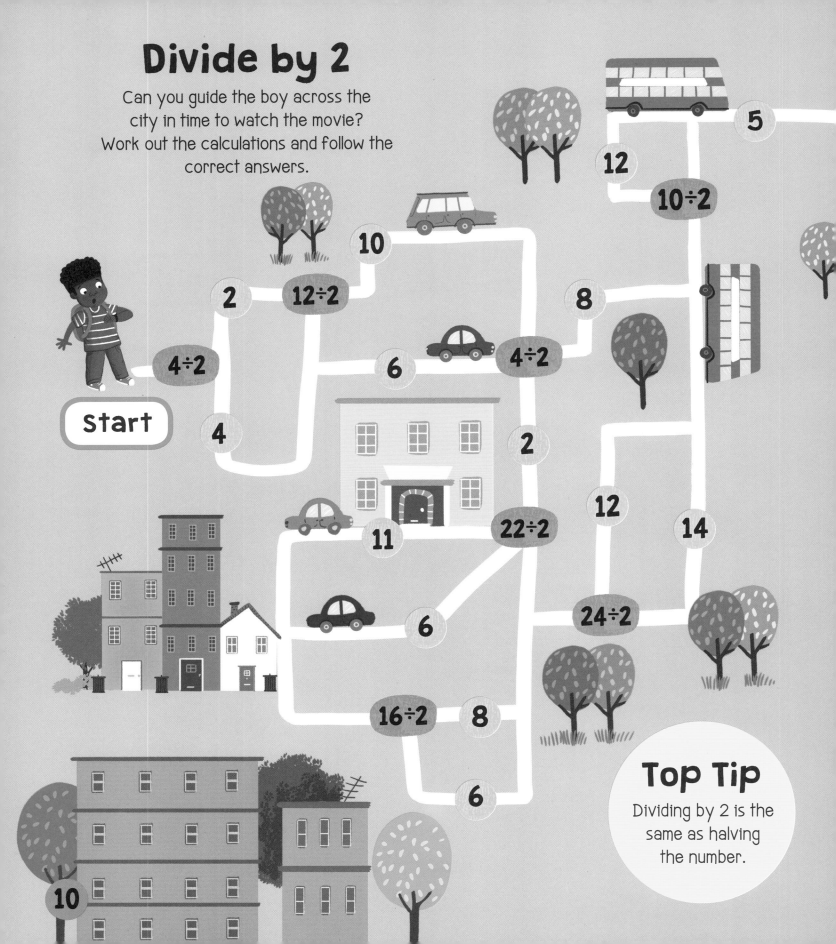

Top Tip

Dividing by 2 is the same as halving the number.

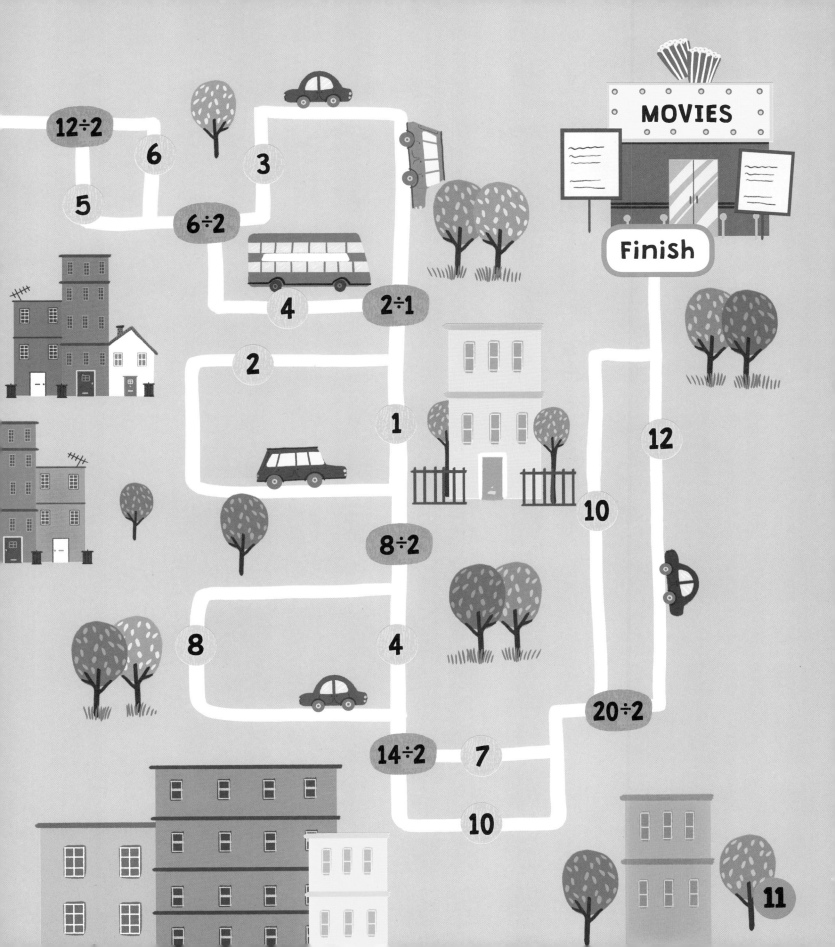

Multiples of 10

Help the knight to find his horse. Follow all of the numbers that are multiples of 10.

Start

45

45

70

90

29

35

56

40

30

Top Tip
Multiples of ten end in 0.

75

32

80

85

81

10

65

50

20

120

Finish

110

Multiples of 10

The boy is eager to start skiing.
Can you guide him to the ski lift?
Work out the calculations.

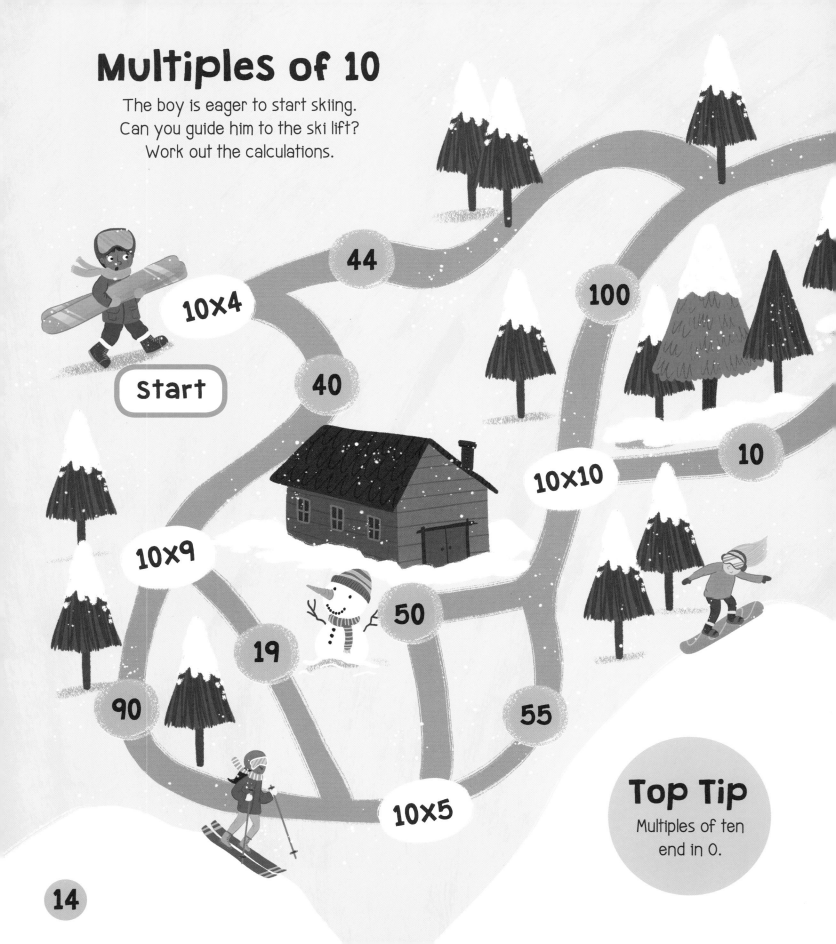

44

100

10X4

Start

40

10

10X10

10X9

50

19

90

55

10X5

Top Tip
Multiples of ten end in 0.

14

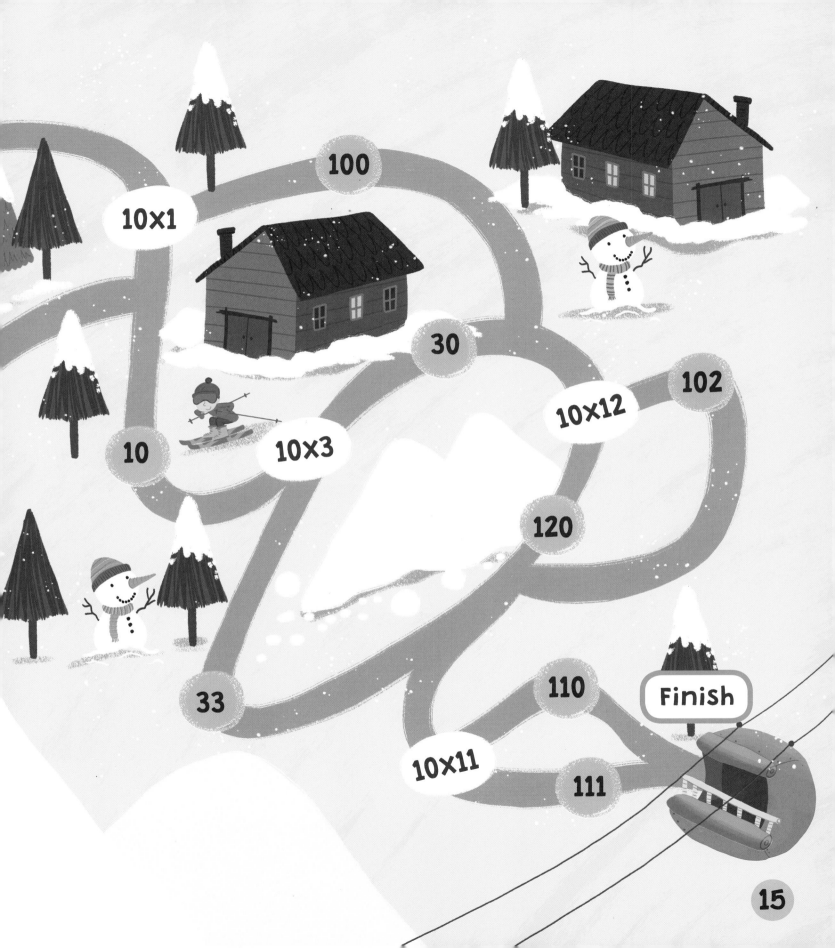

100

10X1

30

102

10X12

10

10X3

120

33

110

Finish

10X11

111

15

Divide by 10

The elephant wants a drink. Can you lead him to the water?
Solve the problems and follow the correct answers to reach the waterfall.

Start

10

40÷10

5

50÷10

70÷10

500

4

70

Top Tip
Remember division
is the opposite of
multiplication:
7 x 10 = 70
70 ÷ 10 = 7

20

120÷10

12

3

30÷10

6

16

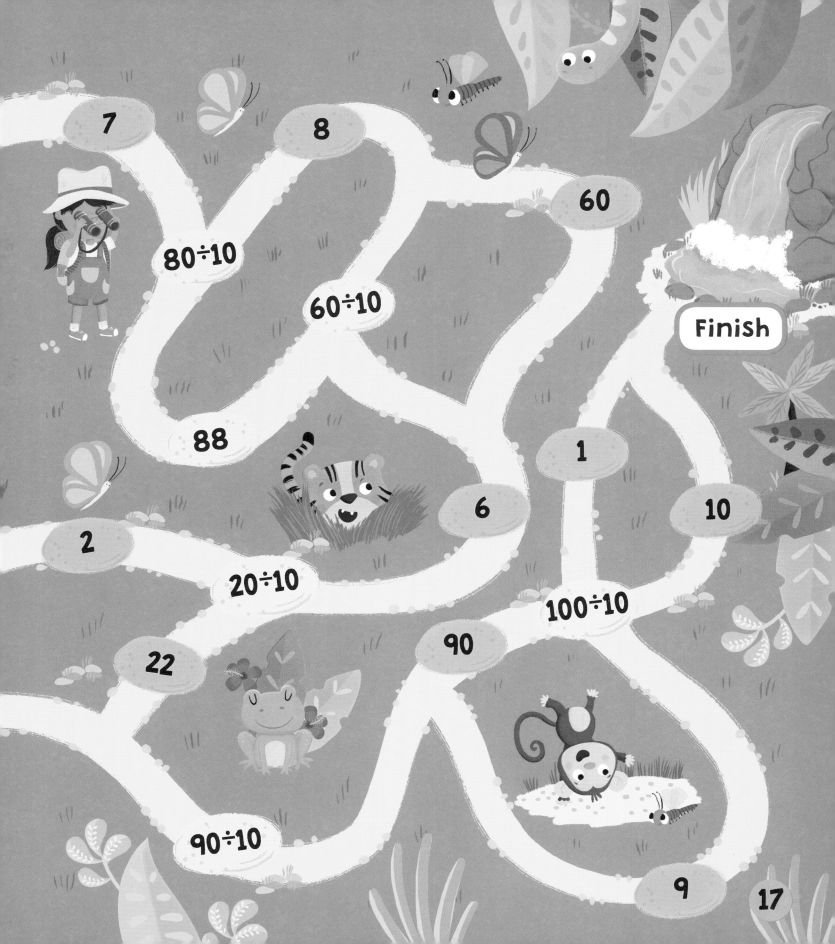

Multiples of 5

Lead the camel across the desert.
Follow the numbers that are multiples of 5.

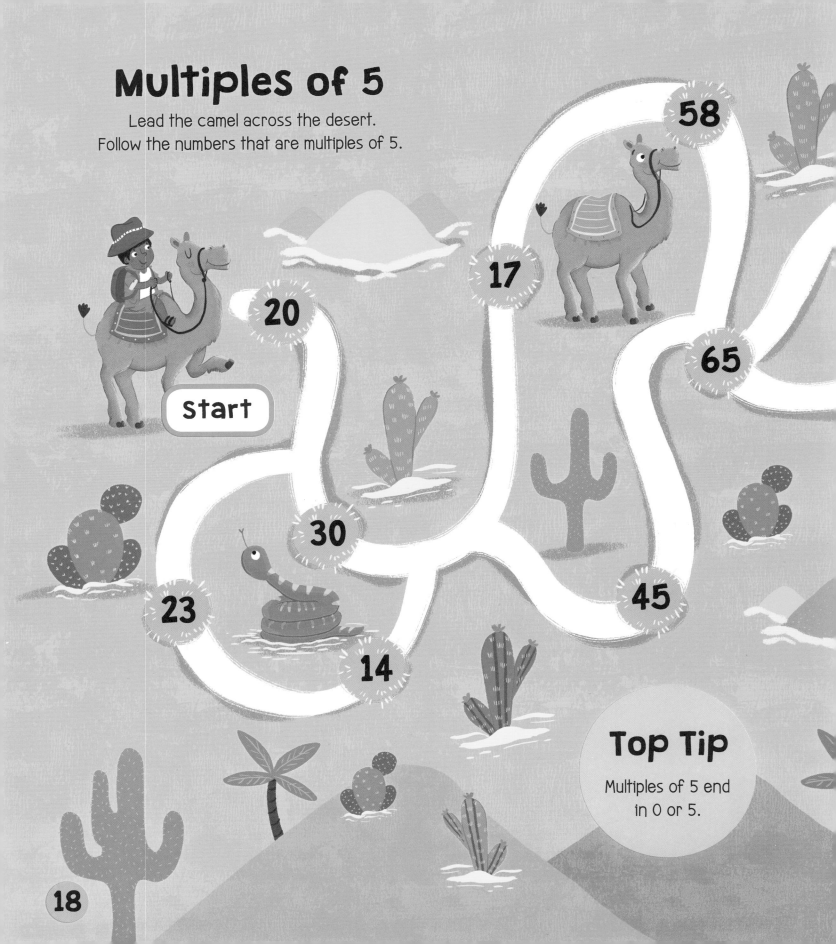

start

58

17

65

20

30

45

23

14

Top Tip

Multiples of 5 end
in 0 or 5.

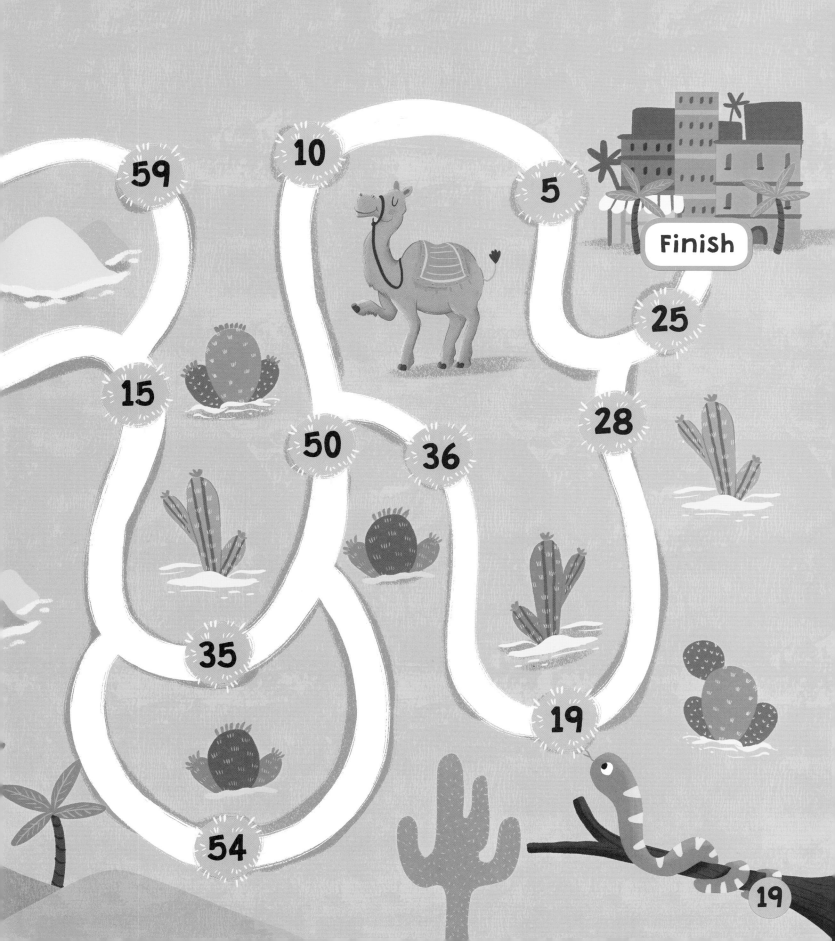

Multiples of 5

Guide the children out of the maze. Solve the calculations and follow the route with the correct answers.

5X1

20

5X4

5

55

25

Start

5X5

35

25

30

5X7

Top Tip

Try counting in 5s.

Divide by 5

Can you guide the little fish away from the shark before it's too late? Solve the calculations and follow the trail with the correct answers.

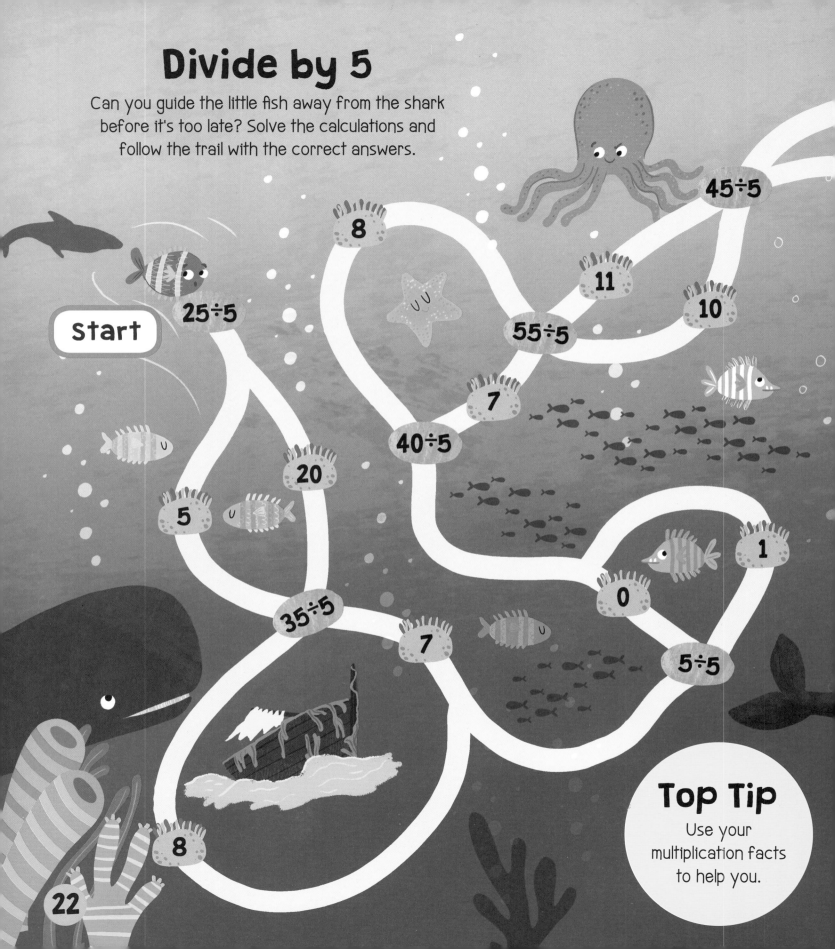

Start

25÷5

8

45÷5

11

55÷5

10

7

40÷5

20

5

1

0

35÷5

7

5÷5

8

22

Top Tip
Use your multiplication facts to help you.

Mixed multiples 2, 5, and 10

Can you show the girl to the music room in time for her music lesson? Solve the multiplication problems and follow the correct answers.

Start

2x10

50

15

50

10x5

20

4

2x5

10

2x2

8

7

2x

24

Mixed division 2, 5, and 10

By solving the calculations and following the correct answers, lead the children to the ice cream van on the beach.

40

45÷5

8

20÷5

5

80÷10

4

2

5

11

4

55÷5

25÷5

Start

Top Tip

Make sure you share by the correct amount.

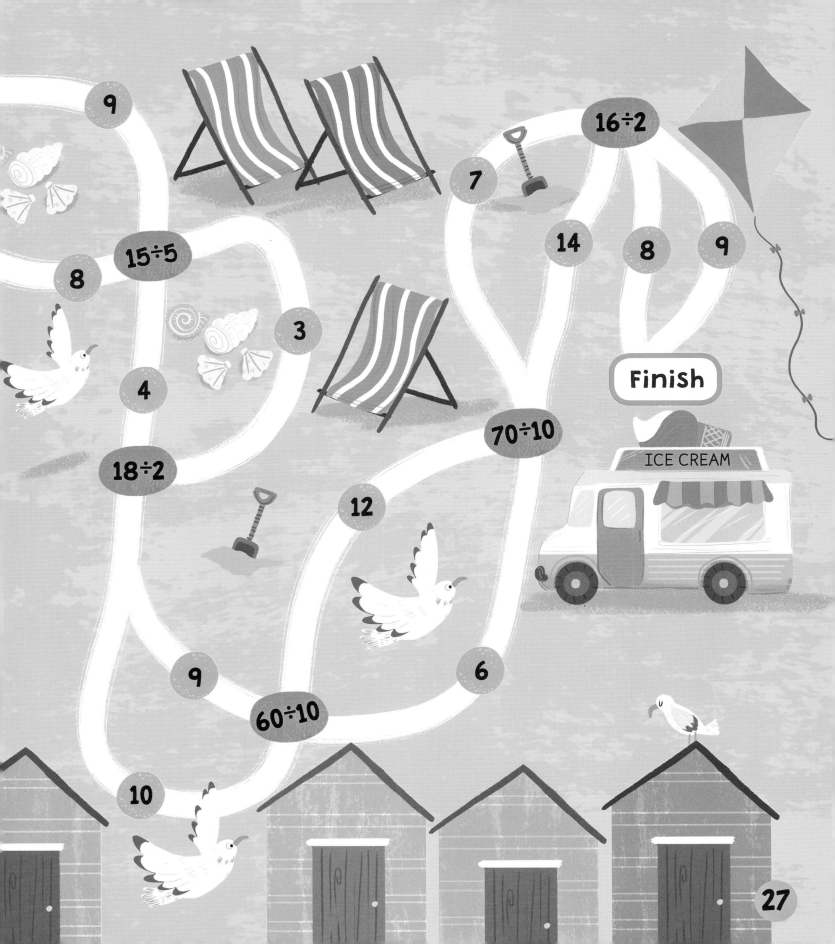

Multiples of 4

Follow the numbers that are multiples of 4 and guide the children to the sandpit to play.

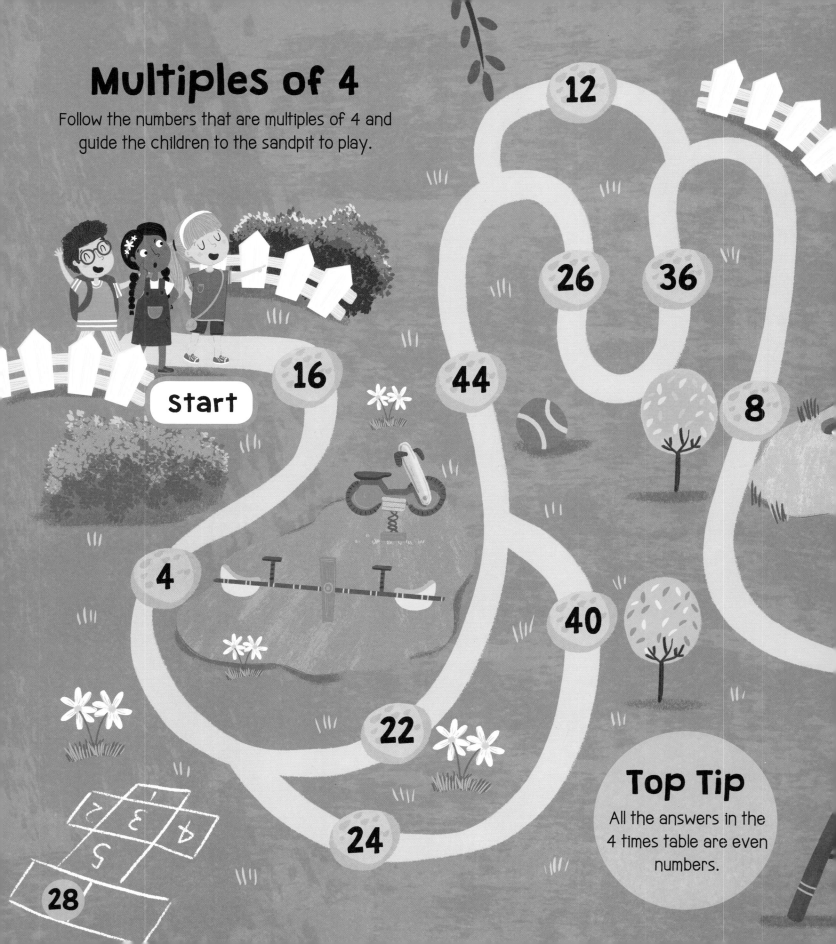

12

26   36

16   44   8

Start

4

40

22

Top Tip

24   All the answers in the
4 times table are even
numbers.

28

Multiples of 4

Can you navigate around the map to find the elephant enclosure at the zoo? Solve the multiplication problems and follow the route with the correct answers.

31

26

4x8

32

4x7

28

4x12

36

Start

4x9

34

Top Tip

Multiplying by 4 is the same as doubling and doubling again:
(7 + 7) + (7 + 7) = 28

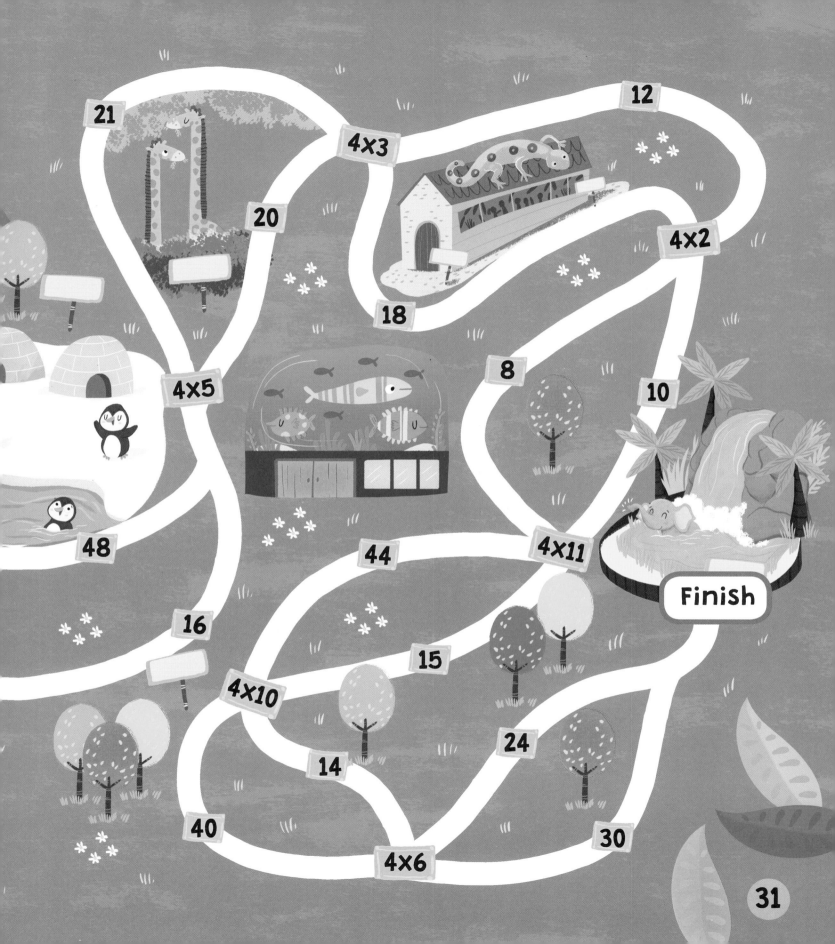

21

4×3

12

20

4×2

18

4×5

8

10

48

4×11

44

Finish

16

15

4×10

24

14

40

30

4×6

31

Divide by 4

Can you guide the train through the countryside to the station? Solve the problems and follow the path with the correct answers.

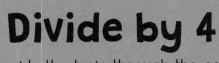
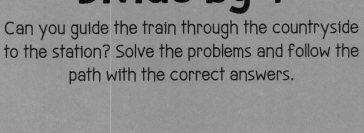

Start

36 ÷ 4

8

32 ÷ 4

8

8

7

48 ÷ 4

7

28 ÷ 4

9

Top Tip

Use your knowledge of the 4 times table to help you:

32 ÷ 4 = 8

8 x 4 = 32

5

12 20÷4

11

4 16÷4 3

8÷4 4

11 40÷4 0 24÷4 7

4 48 6

44÷4

2 10 **Finish**

33

Multiples of 8

Follow the numbers that are multiples of 8 and guide the ants across the garden and back to their nest.

start

Top Tip

If you can't remember your 8 times table, double the answers in the 4 times table.

20

48

64

8

56

18

10

16

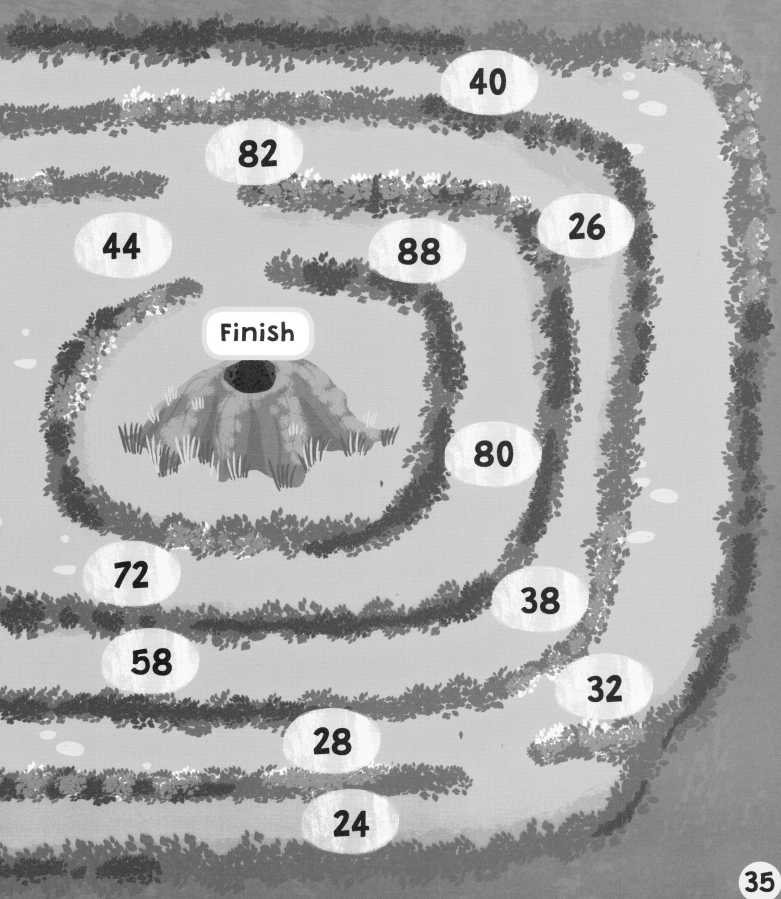

Multiples of 8

Answer the calculations and follow the trail with the correct answers to help the dinosaur find her eggs before the volcano erupts!

64

8X6

8X8

10

68

16

8X2

35

40

80

Start

8X5

8X4

18

30

32

36

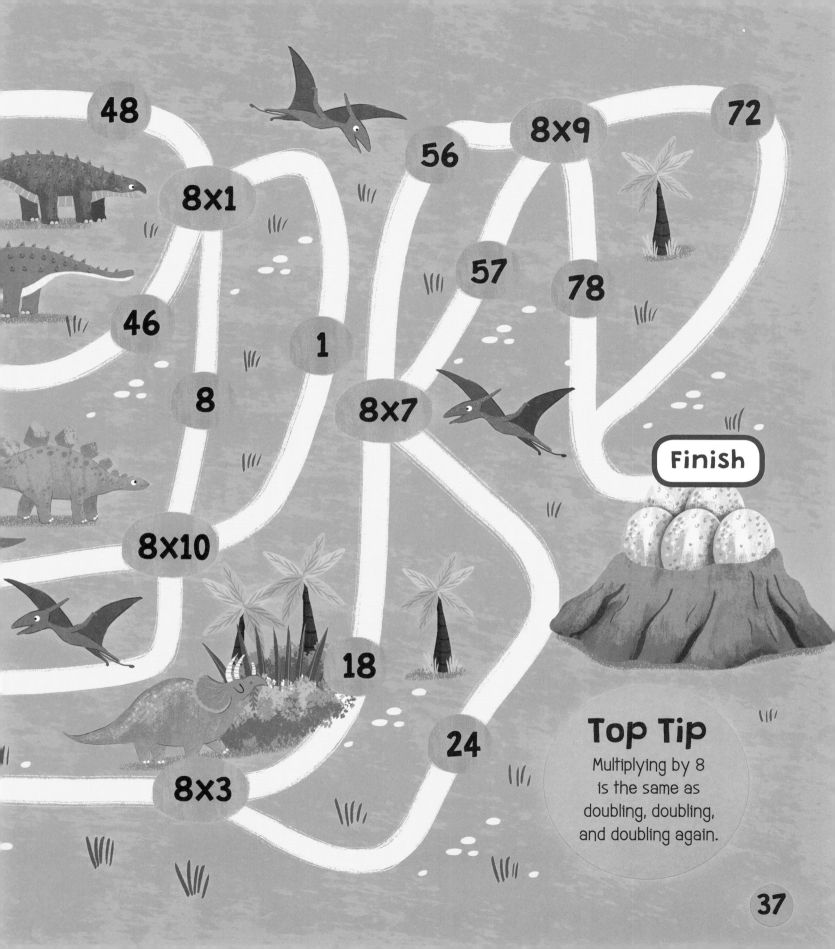

48

8x1

56

8x9

72

46

1

57

78

8

8x7

Finish

8x10

18

24

8x3

Top Tip
Multiplying by 8
is the same as
doubling, doubling,
and doubling again.

37

Divide by 8

Solve the problems and follow the route with the correct answers to lead the shoppers to the check out.

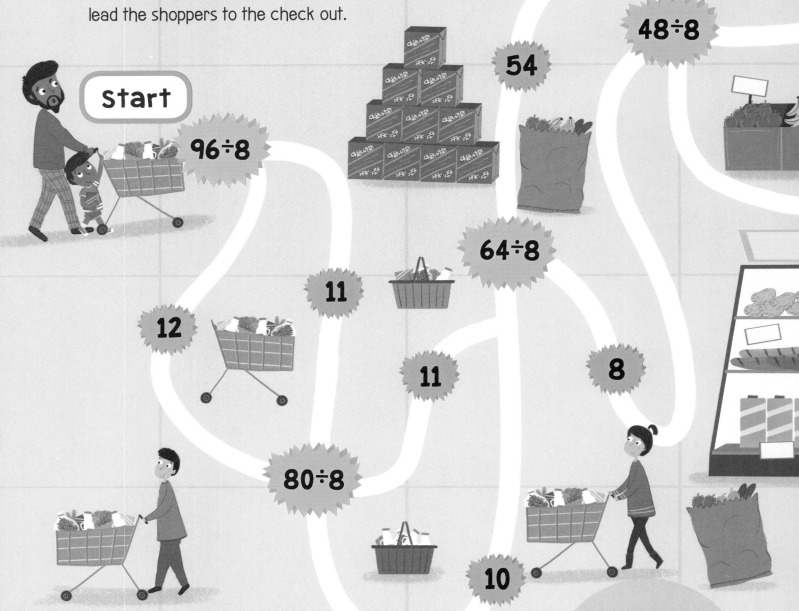

Start

96÷8

54

48÷8

11

64÷8

12

11

8

80÷8

10

Top Tip

Dividing by 8 can be tricky. Try halving, halving, and halving again.

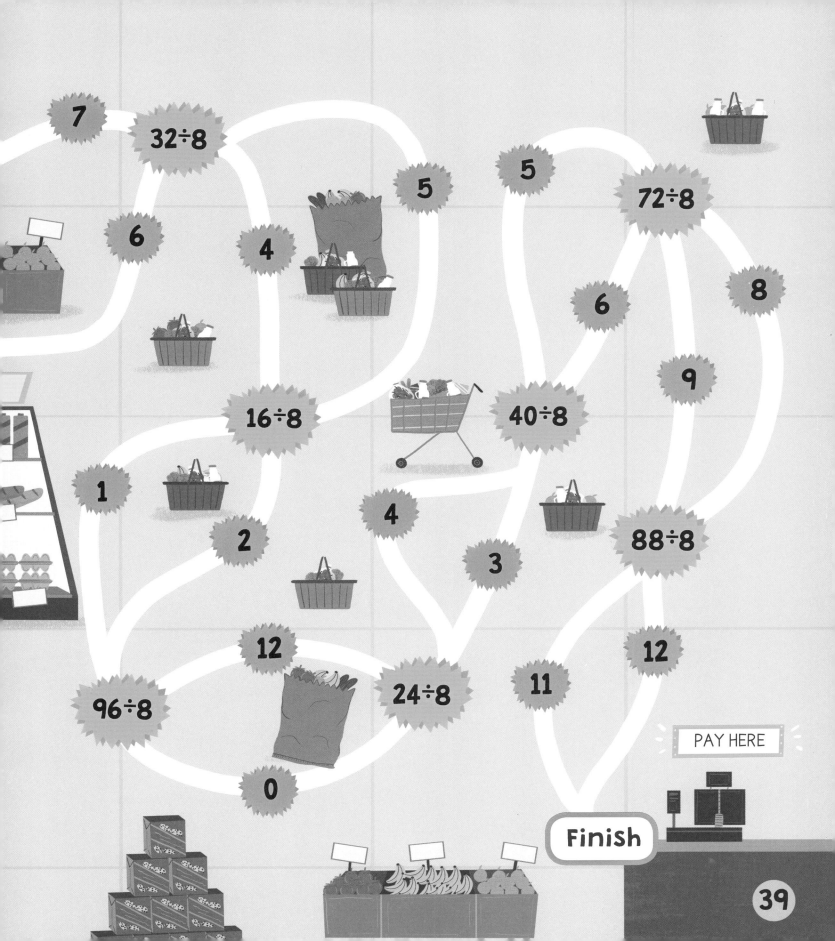

7

32÷8

6

5

4

5

72÷8

6

8

9

16÷8

40÷8

1

2

4

88÷8

3

12

11

12

96÷8

24÷8

0

PAY HERE

Finish

39

Mixed multiples 2, 4, and 8

Speed through the number problems and follow the correct answers to get the family to the airport in time!

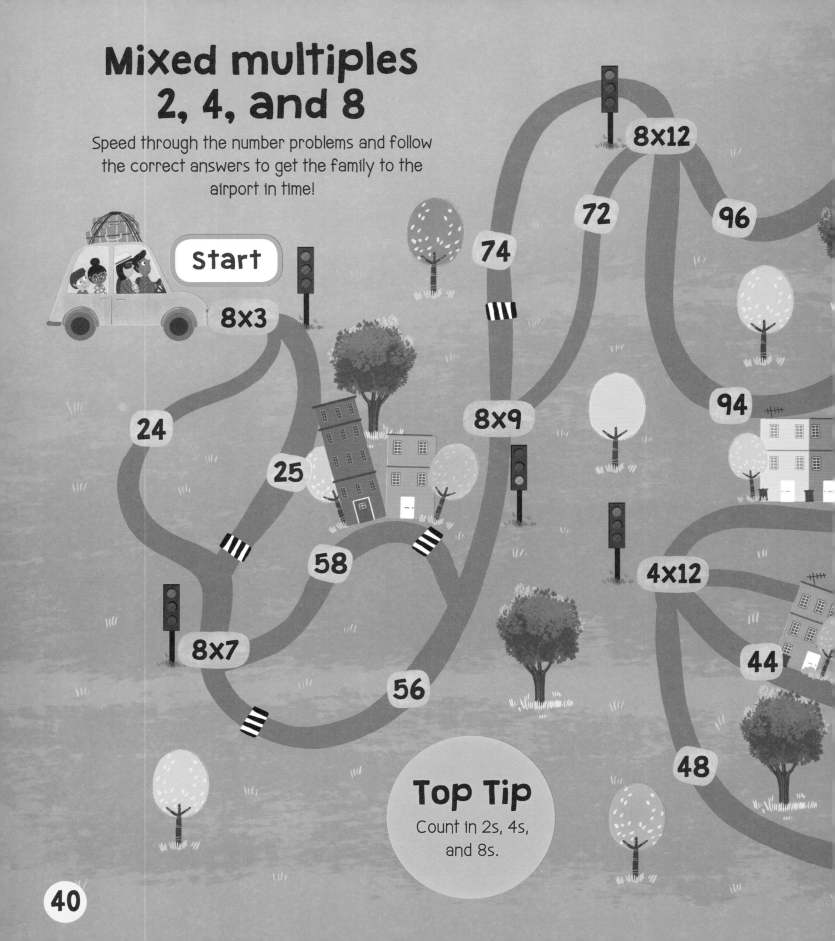

Start

8×3

8×12

72

96

74

24

25

8×9

94

58

4×12

8×7

56

44

48

Top Tip

Count in 2s, 4s, and 8s.

Mixed division 2, 4, and 8

Solve the problems and follow the path with the correct answers to lead the fox back to his den.

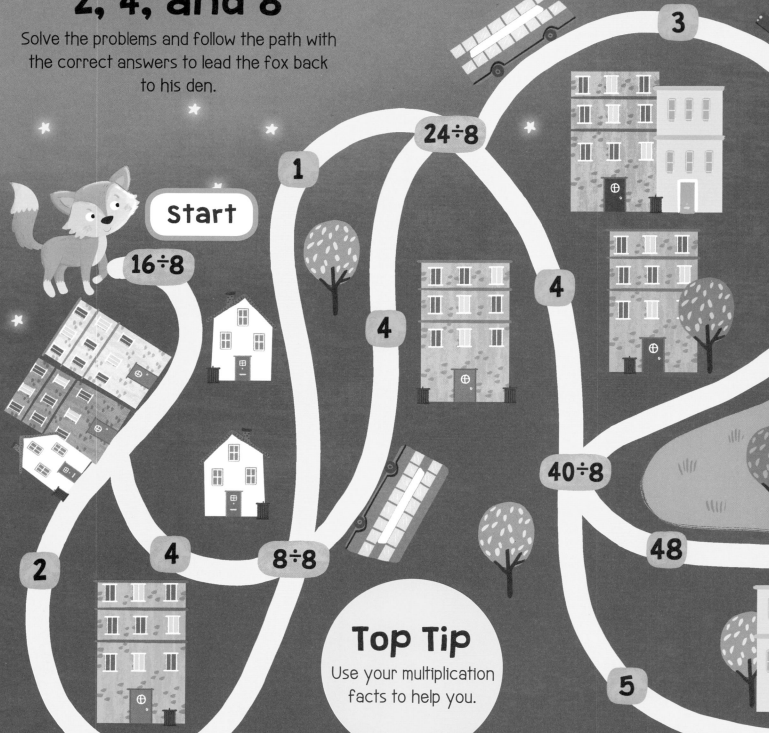

Start

16÷8

24÷8

1

3

4

4

40÷8

8÷8

48

2

4

5

Top Tip

Use your multiplication facts to help you.

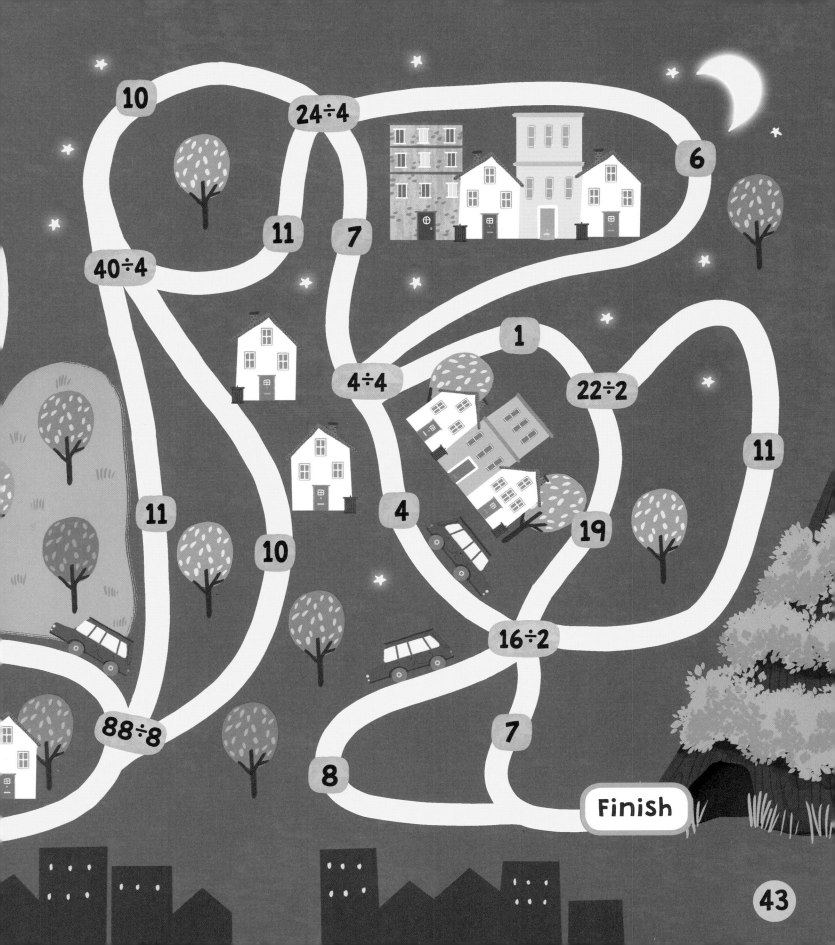

10

24÷4

6

11 7

40÷4

1

22÷2

4÷4

11

4

19

11

10

16÷2

88÷8

7

8

Finish

43

Multiples of 3

Puff along the tracks following the numbers that are multiples of 3 to guide the steam train to the station.

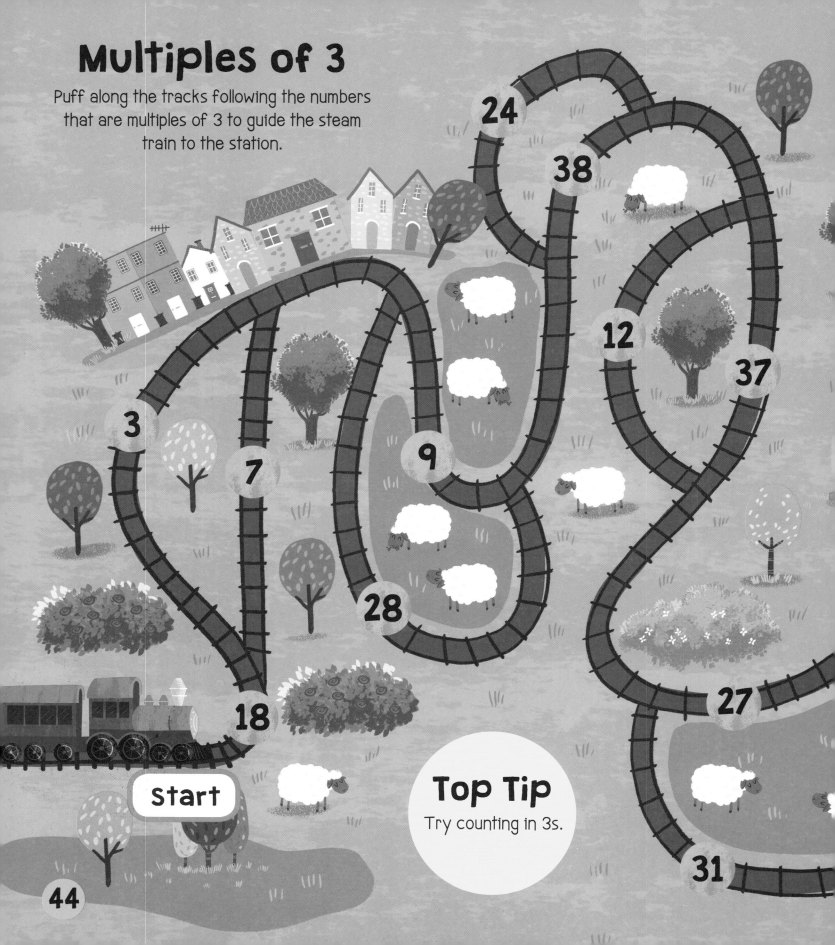

24

38

12

37

3

7

9

28

27

18

Start

Top Tip
Try counting in 3s.

31

44

More multiples of 3

Solve the calculations and follow the way with the correct answers to help the rocket land on the moon.

Start

3x4

24

11

3x5

8

3x8

13

9

15

10

12

3x3

3x11

14

33

Top Tip

Remember that
3 x 4 =
3 + 3 + 3 + 3

3x12

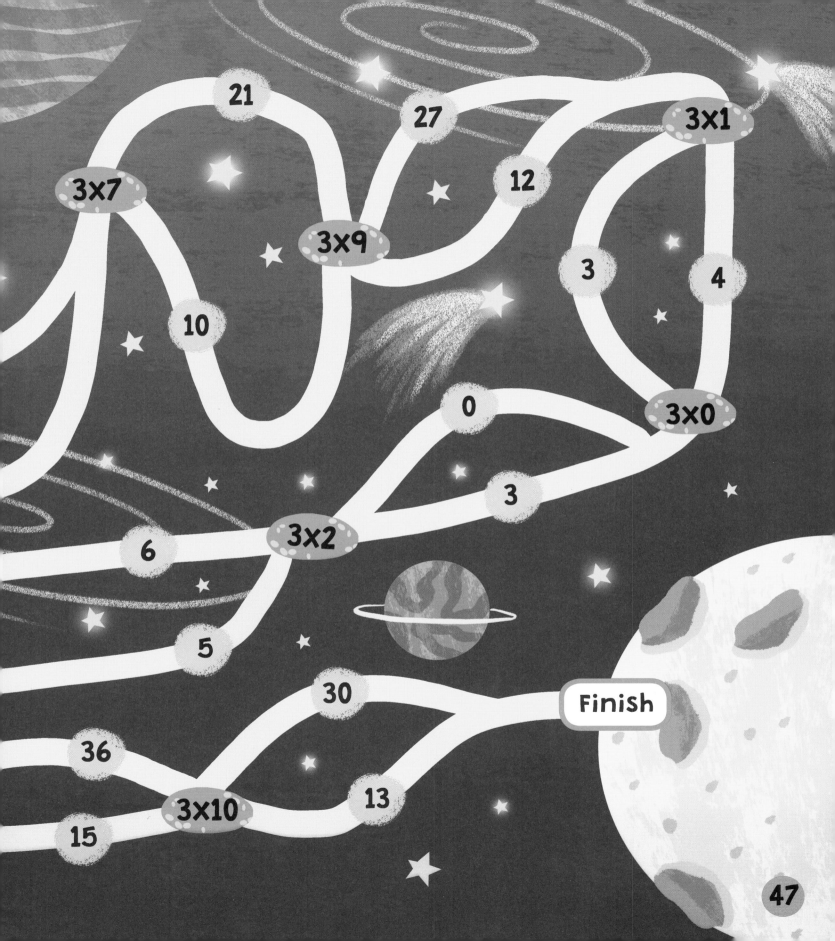

21

27

3×1

3×7

12

3×9

3

4

10

3×0

0

3

6

3×2

5

30

Finish

36

13

3×10

15

47

Divide by 3

Guide the children through the roads by following the route with the correct answers.

12

12

18÷3

Start

33÷3

11

36÷3

15

24

6

27÷3

9

30÷3

10

4

20

Top Tip

Share into three equal groups.

6÷3

Finish

5

2

3

6

24÷3

3

4

15÷3

7

12÷3

8

7

21÷3

9÷3

3

8

4

49

Multiples of 6

Ride the roller coaster back to the finish.
Follow the numbers that are multiples
of 6 to go the right way.

start

6

34

30

36

24

56

12

18

46

50

44

POPCORN

BURGERS

Top Tip

If you multiply 6 by
an even number, the
answer will end with
the same digit as
that number.

More multiples of 6

Help the boy find the bouncy castle at the funfair. Solve the multiplication problems and follow the path with the correct answers.

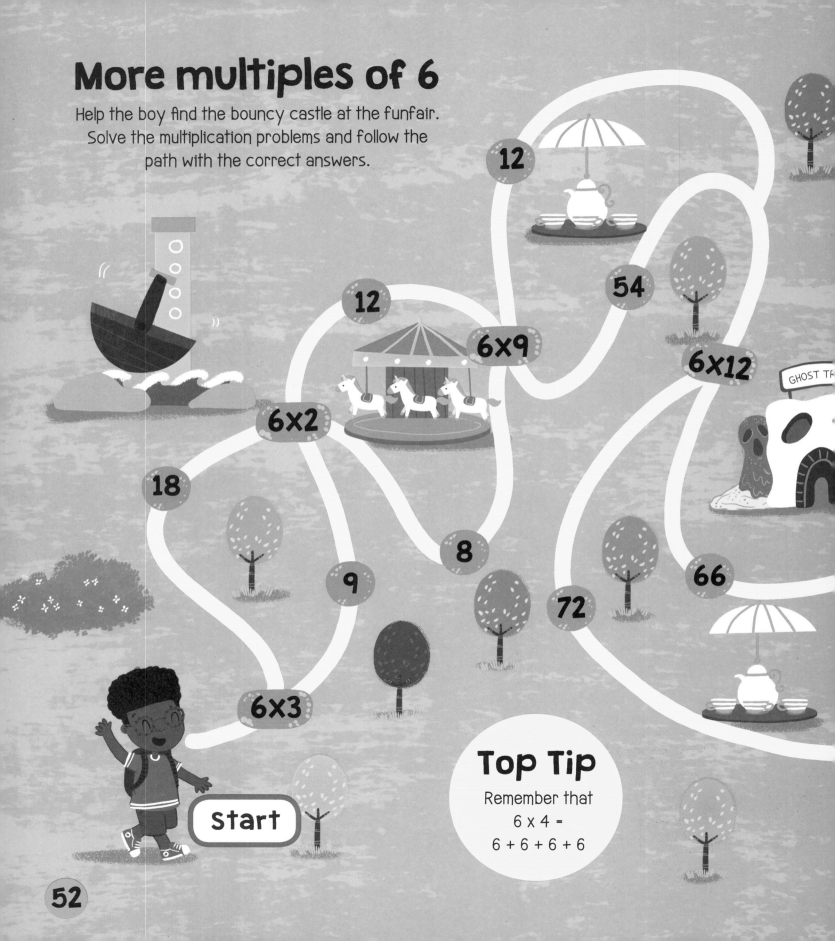

12

12

54

6x9

6x12

GHOST TR

6x2

18

8

9

66

72

6x3

Start

Top Tip
Remember that
6 x 4 =
6 + 6 + 6 + 6

Divide by 6

Help the police catch the burglars by solving the calculations and following the correct answers.

9

60÷6

10

30÷6

5

24÷6

5

7

8

6

4

66÷6

12

11

42÷6

Start

54

36÷6

10

72÷6   12

6   7   1   6   54÷6

8   9

48÷6   7   6÷6

12÷6

3   2

8

Finish

55

Multiples of 9

Follow the numbers that are multiples of 9 to lead the scientist to the exit: it's time for a lunch break.

27

18

14

Start

9

102

25

56

63

Top Tip

Add up the digits in the solutions for 1 x 9 to 9 x 9. The answer is always 9!

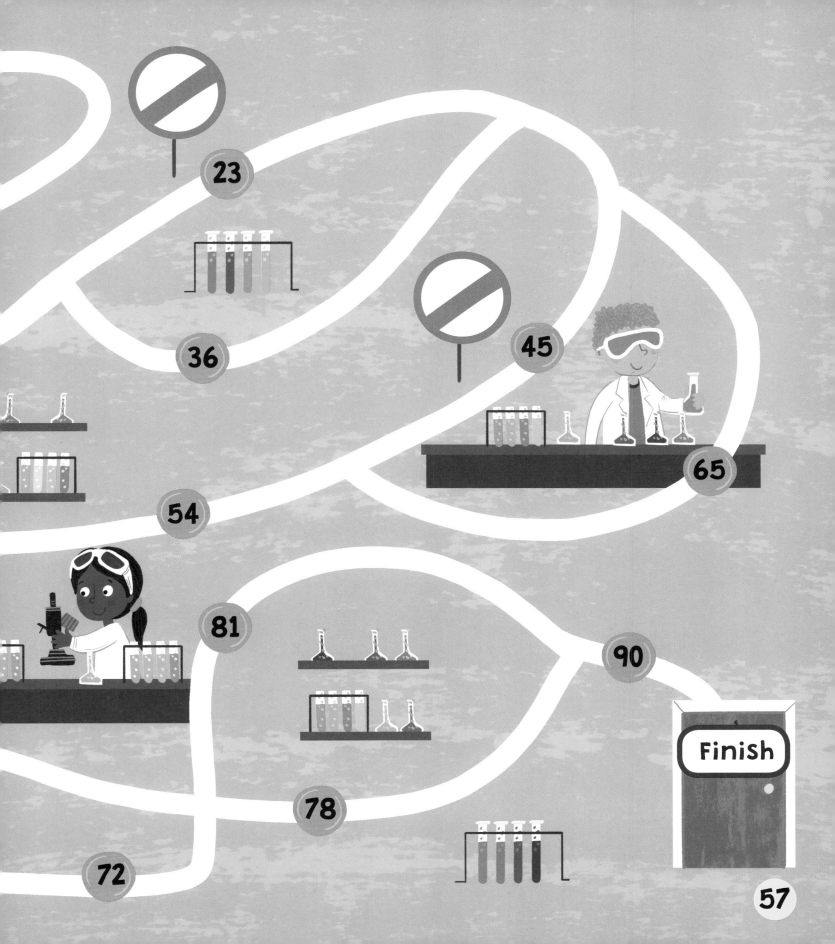

More multiples of 9

Solve the calculations and follow the correct answers to help the helicopter to safely reach the landing pad.

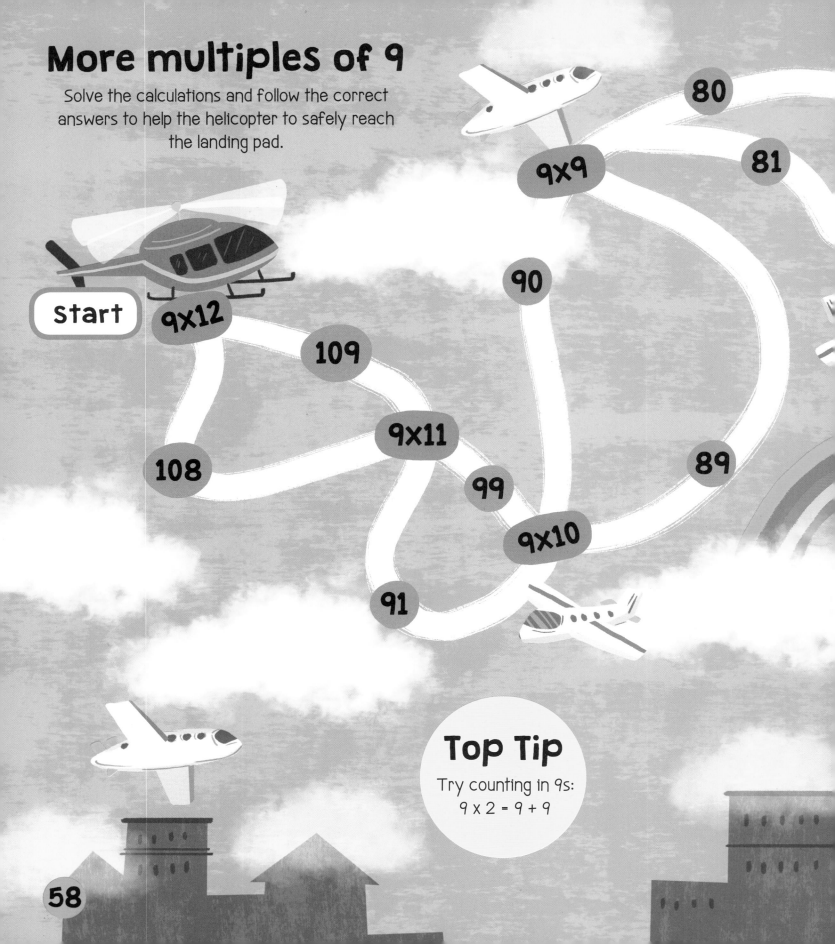

Start

9x12

9x9

80

81

90

109

9x11

108

99

89

9x10

91

Top Tip

Try counting in 9s:
9 x 2 = 9 + 9

58

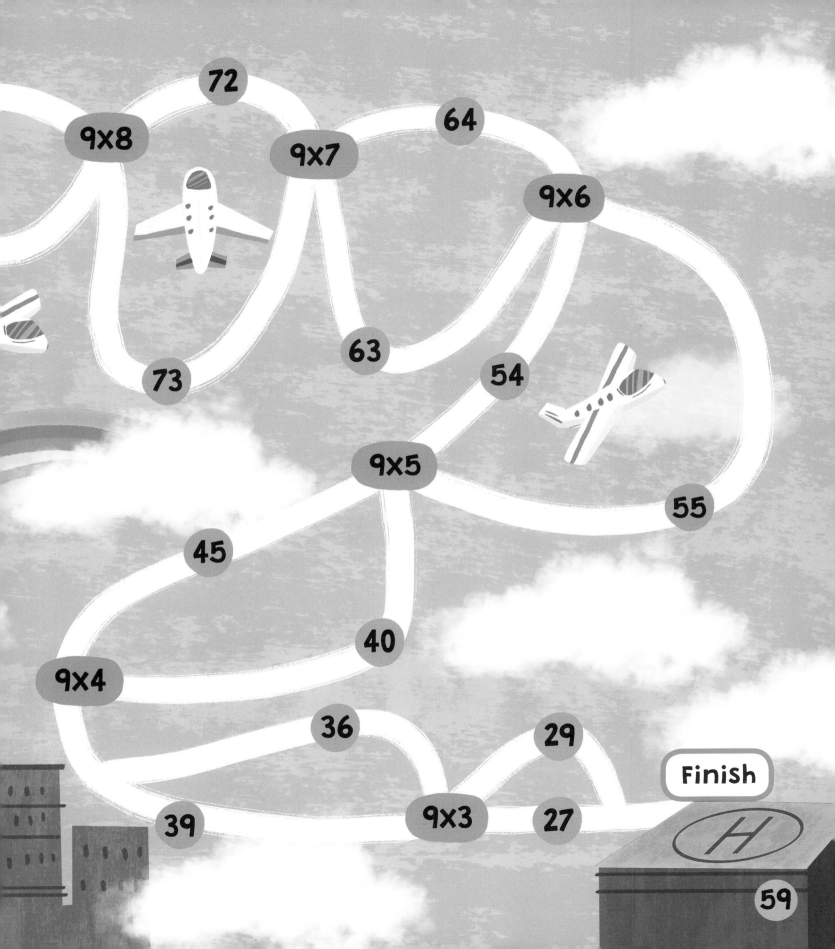

Divide by 9

Help the clown to find his juggling balls by solving the problems and following the correct answers.

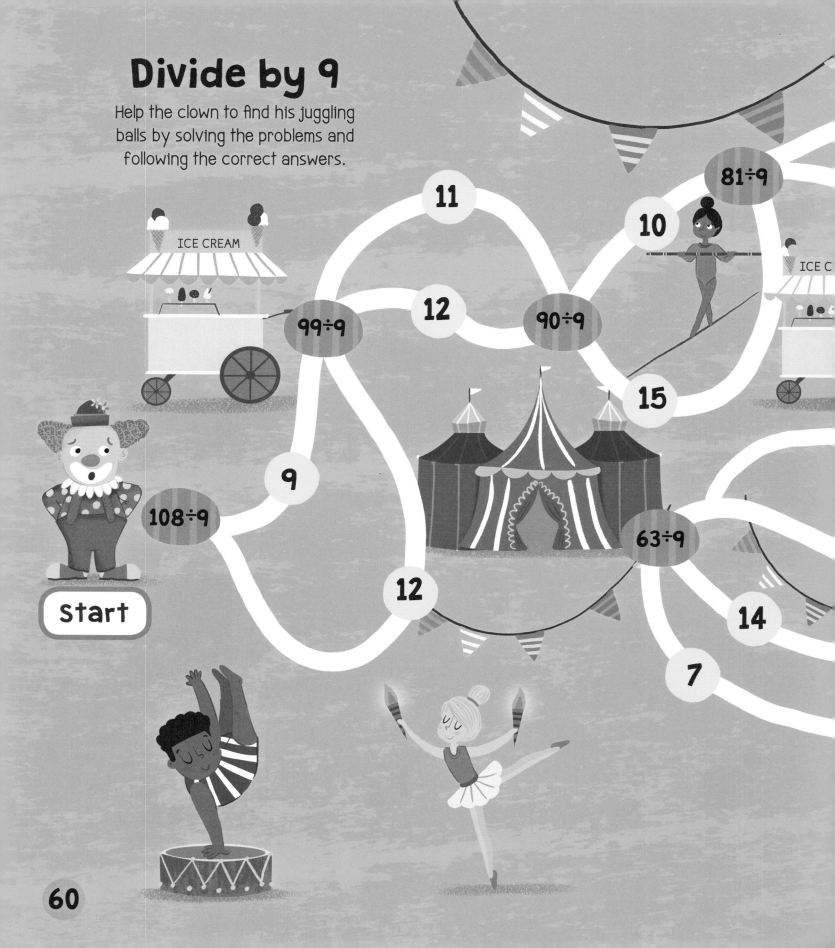

ICE CREAM

ICE C

11

10

81÷9

12

99÷9

90÷9

15

9

108÷9

63÷9

12

14

7

Start

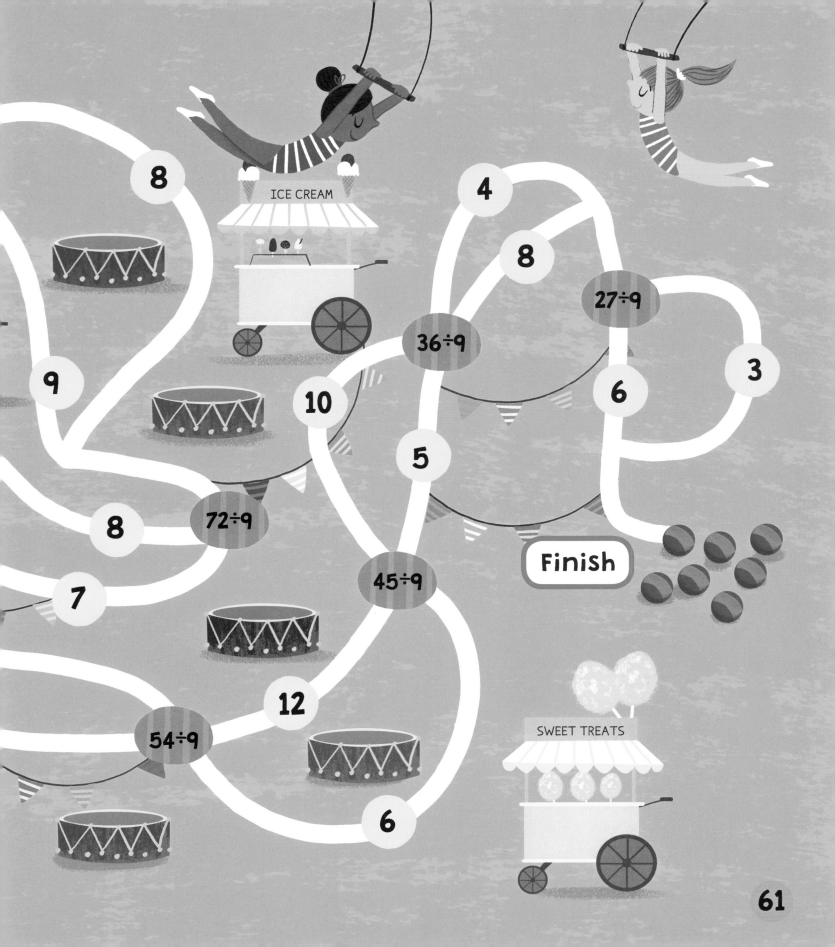

Mixed multiples of 3, 6, and 9

Help the pirate find the treasure.
Solve the calculations and follow the
correct answers.

19

9x1

9x2

27

18

29

9x3

39

27

3x9

Start

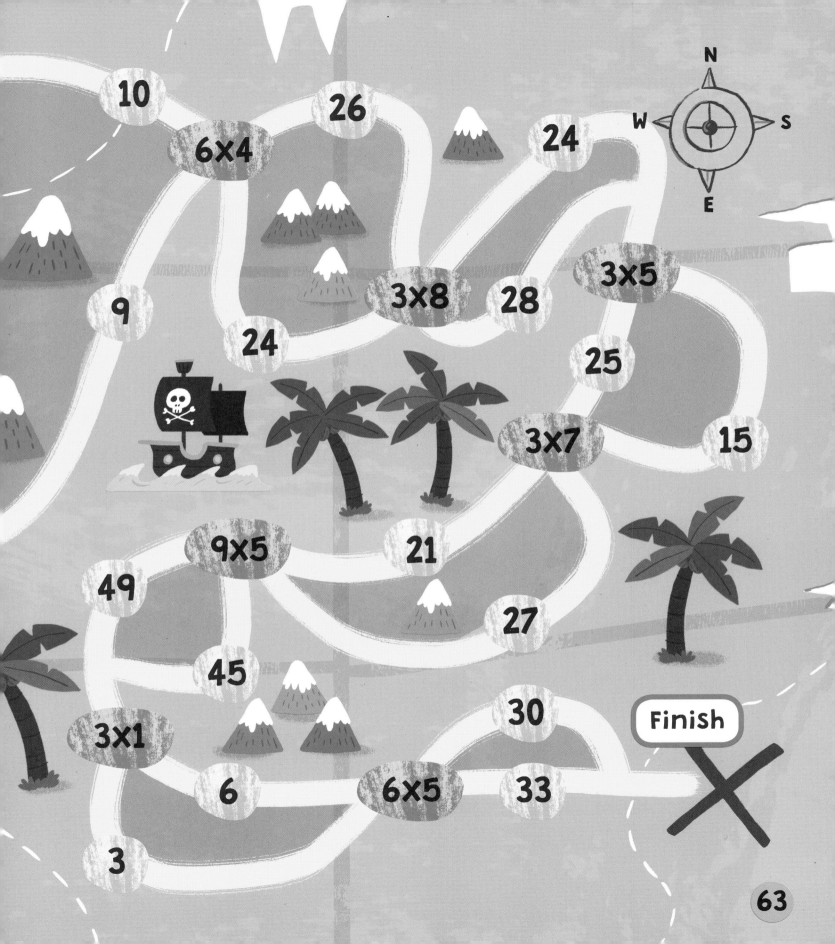

10

26

24

6X4

9

3X8

28

3X5

24

25

3X7

15

9X5

49

21

45

27

3X1

30

Finish

6

6X5

33

3

63

Divide and multiply 3, 6, and 9

The delivery van needs help delivering the parcels. Solve the calculations and follow the correct answers to guide the truck to the house with the green door.

5

36÷9

6

6

45÷9

7

4

3

54÷9

66÷6

8

63÷9

7

Start

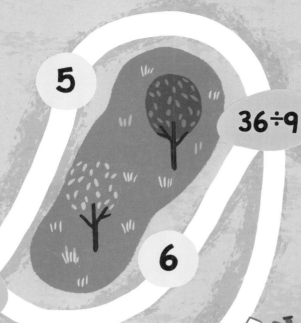

11

36÷6

7

8

10

48÷6

60÷6

6

11

7

3x9

12

23

3x1

27

1

3

3

12÷3

4

Finish

Multiples of 11

Follow the numbers that are multiples of 11 to lead the baby dragon back to his mother.

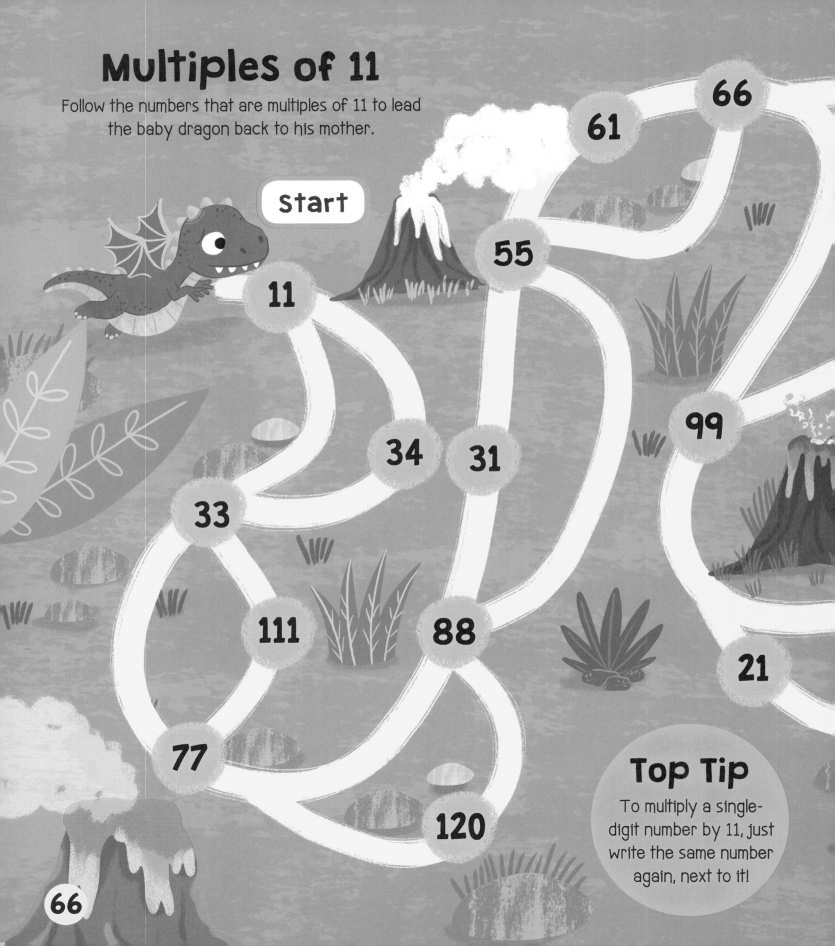

Start

66
61
55
66
99
11
34
31
33
111
88
21
77
120

Top Tip

To multiply a single-digit number by 11, just write the same number again, next to it!

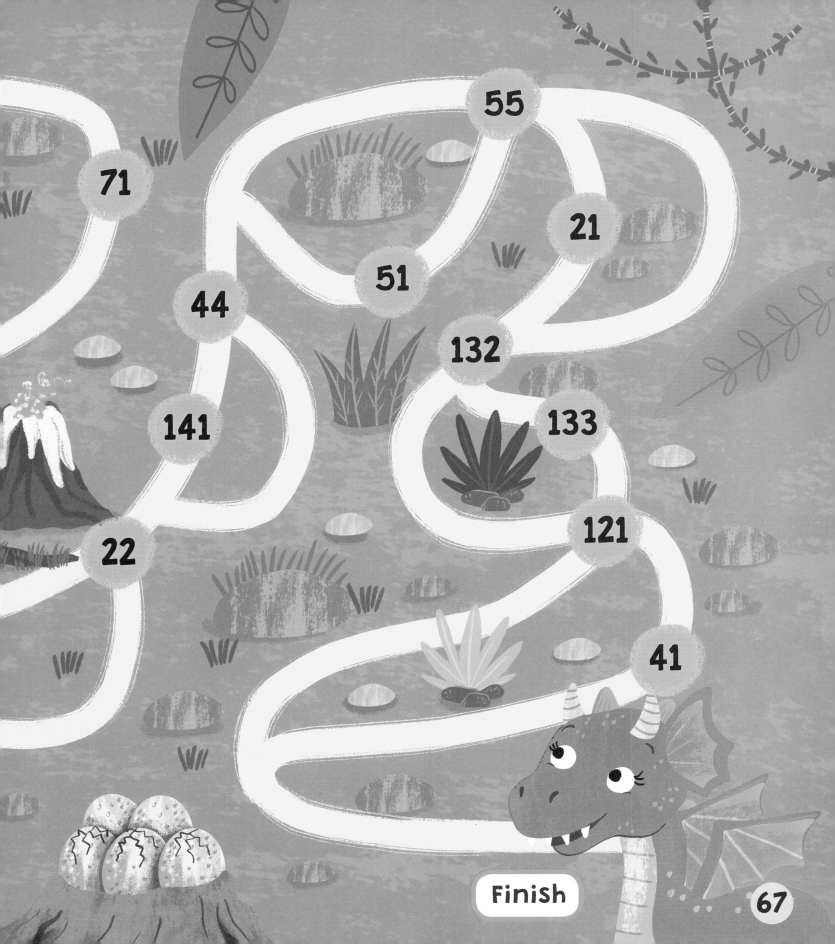

Finish

67

Divide by 11

Guide the mermaid to the pearl by solving the calculations and following the correct answers.

3

4

66÷11

8

33÷11

11

77÷11

6

7

14

4

Start

44÷11

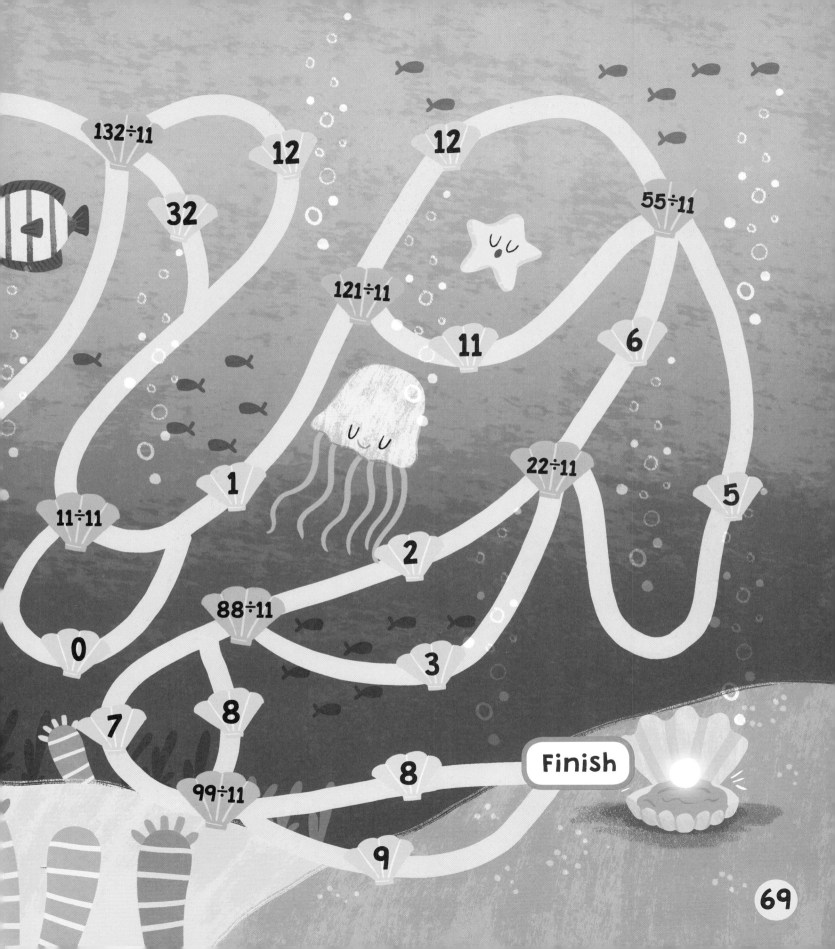

132÷11

12

32

12

55÷11

121÷11

11

6

11÷11

1

22÷11

5

0

2

88÷11

3

7

8

8

Finish

99÷11

9

69

Multiples of 12

Follow the numbers that are multiples of 12 to help the children row back to the campsite.

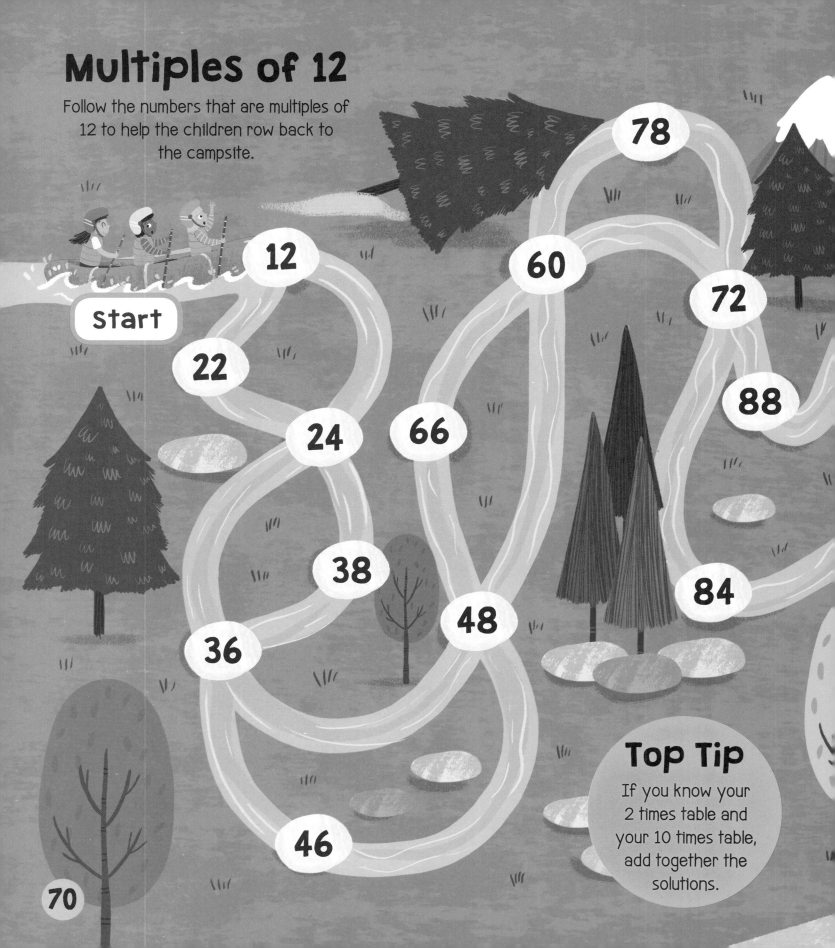

Start

12

78

60

72

88

22

24

66

38

84

48

36

46

70

Top Tip

If you know your 2 times table and your 10 times table, add together the solutions.

96

110

108

120

140

130

132

44

144

8

Finish

Divide by 12

Guide the children to the other end of the campsite. Solve the problems and follow the path with the correct answers.

9

108÷12

20

120÷12

8

13

11

8

10

132÷12

72÷12

5

12

6

14

144÷12

Start

Top Tip
Remember that division is the opposite of multiplication.

72

Mixed 10, 11, 12 multiplication

Speed to the finish line by solving the multiplication questions and follow the path with the correct answers.

Start

10x2

50

15

11x6

10x5

20

12

66

22

24

60

11x2

12x2

21

Top Tip

Watch out: it's mixed multiplication!

22

74

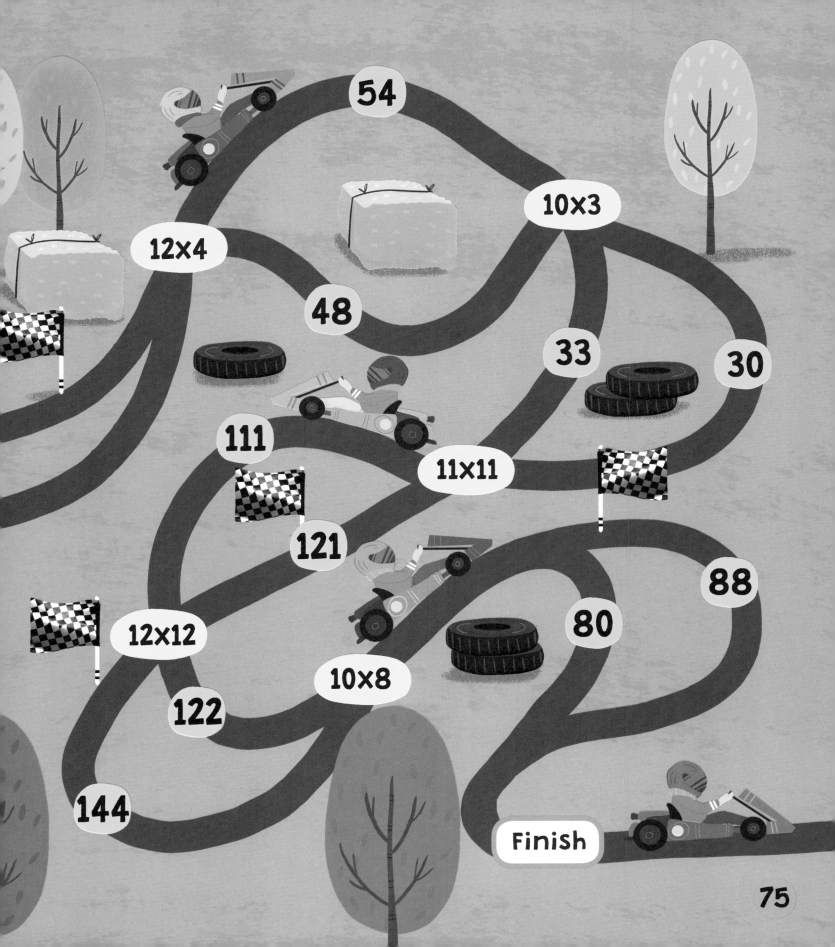

Mixed multiply and divide by 2

Solve the calculations and follow the path with the correct answers to get to the finish line.

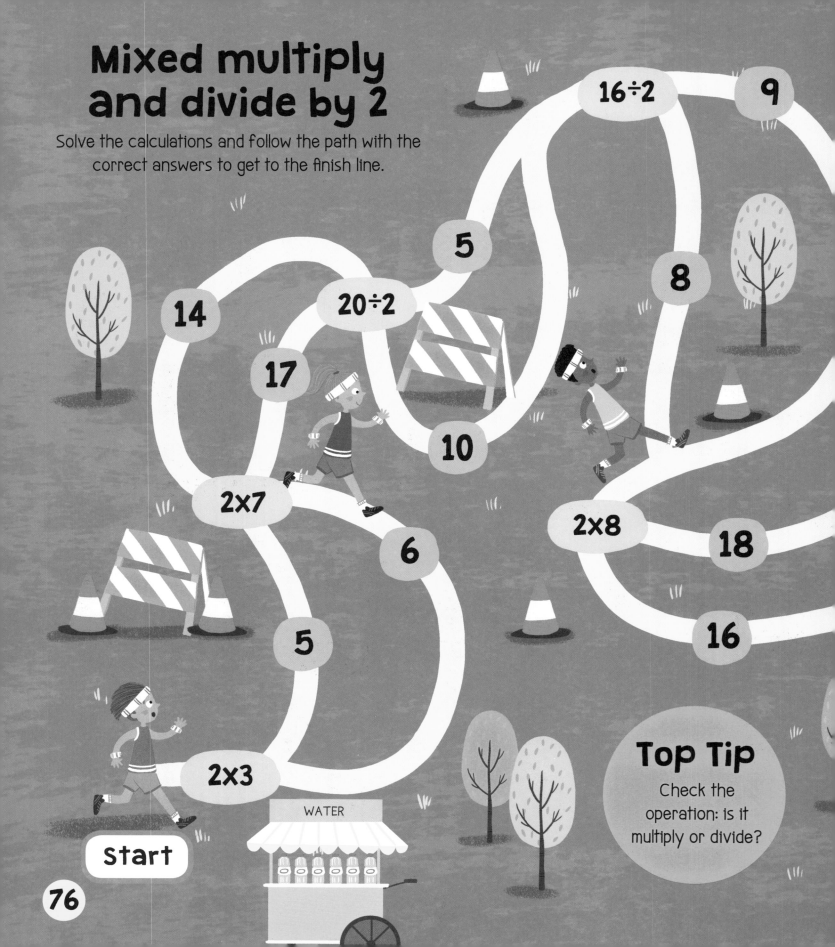

16÷2

9

5

8

14

20÷2

17

10

2×7

2×8

18

6

16

5

2×3

WATER

Start

Top Tip

Check the operation: is it multiply or divide?

76

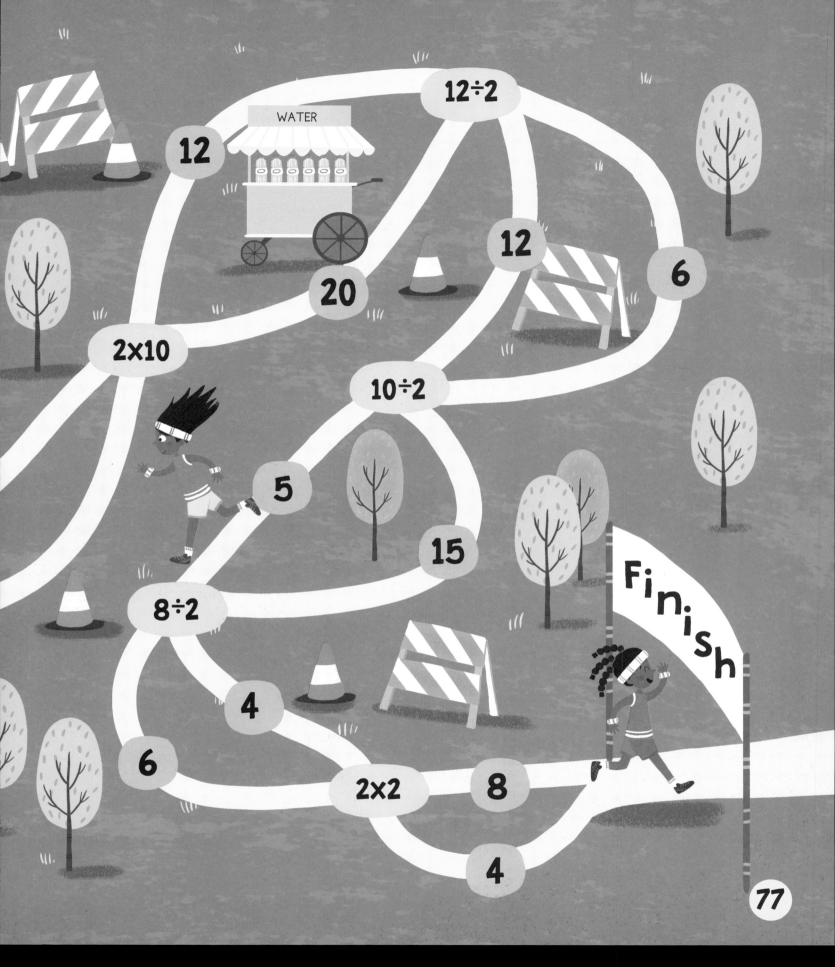

Mixed multiply and divide by 5

Help the boy find his way through the cave by solving the problems, following the route with the correct answers.

Start

25÷5

5×7

37

4

5

5

20

20÷5

8

5×3

15

Top Tip

Multiplying 5 by an odd number gives you an answer ending with 5. Multiplying 5 by an even number give you an answer ending with 0.

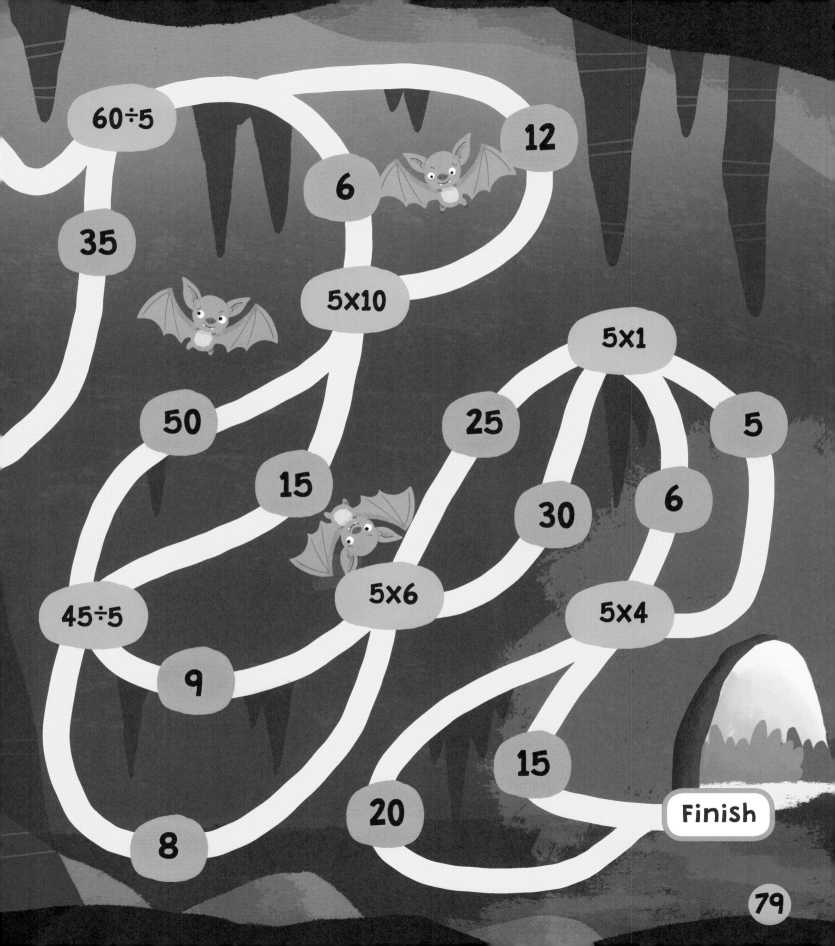

60÷5

12

6

35

5x10

5x1

50

25

5

15

30

6

45÷5

5x6

5x4

9

15

8

20

Finish

Multiples of 100

The girl has dropped her fishing net; follow the numbers that are multiples of 100 to help her find it.

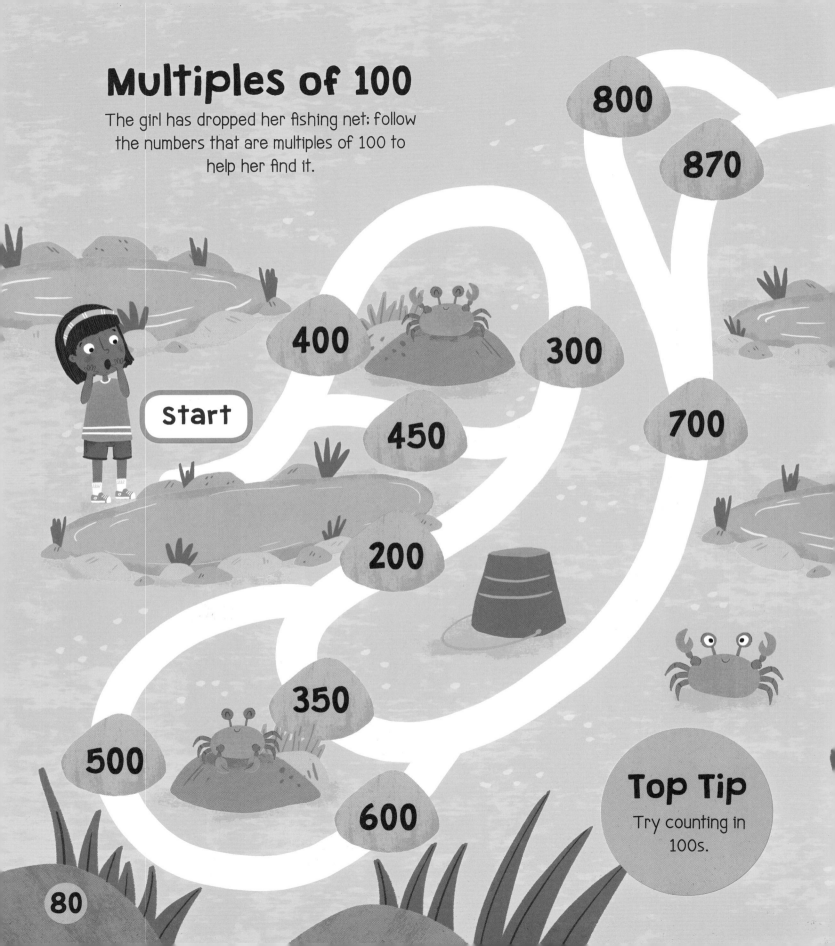

800

870

400

300

start

450

700

200

350

500

600

Top Tip
Try counting in 100s.

80

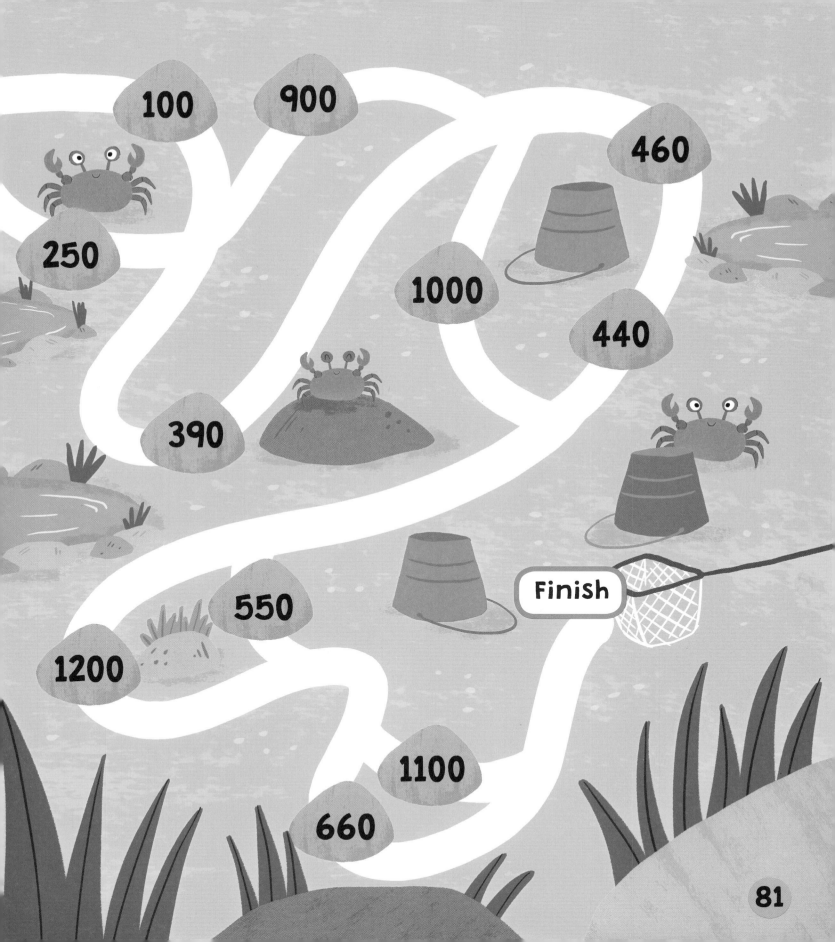

Divide by 100

Guide the fairy through the magical forest and back to the fairy door. Solve the calculations and follow the correct answers.

Start

200÷100

20

2

300÷100

30

3

900÷100

500÷100

9

50

90

Top Tip

Remember division is the opposite of multiplication:
200 ÷ 100 = ?
? x 100 = 200

5

800÷100

3

8

80

30

300÷100

100÷100

400÷100

40

4

1

10

60 600÷100

700÷100

6

7 70

Finish

HOME

83

Multiples of 50

Follow the numbers that are multiples of 50 to help the fly escape the spiders' web.

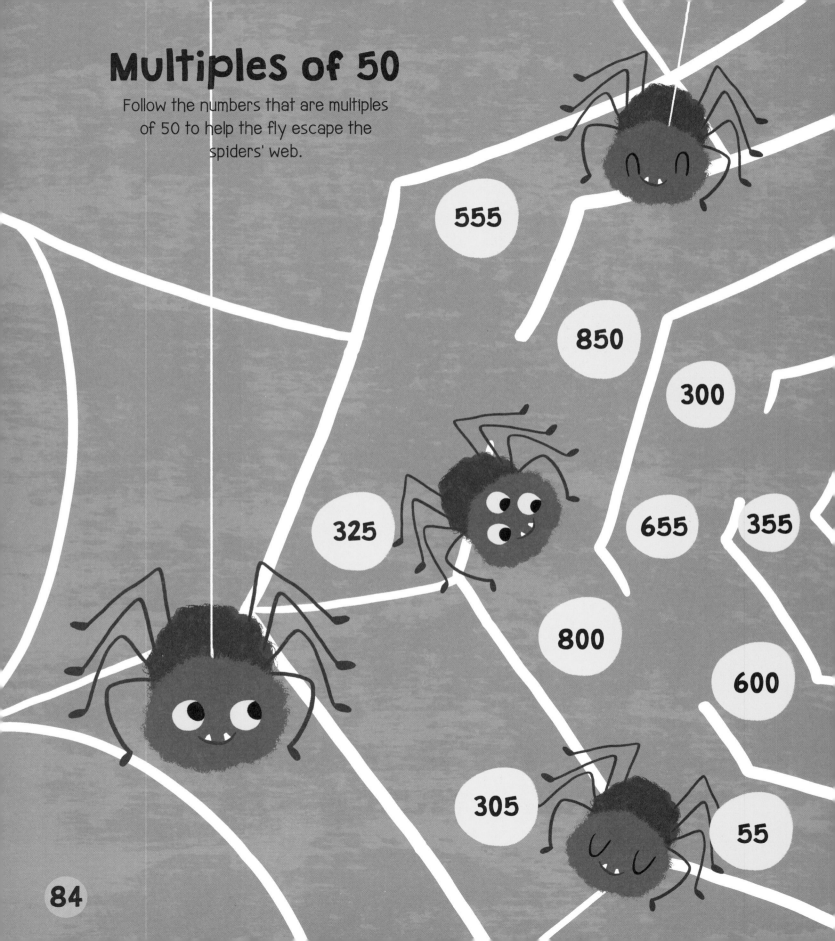

555

850

300

325

655

355

800

600

305

55

84

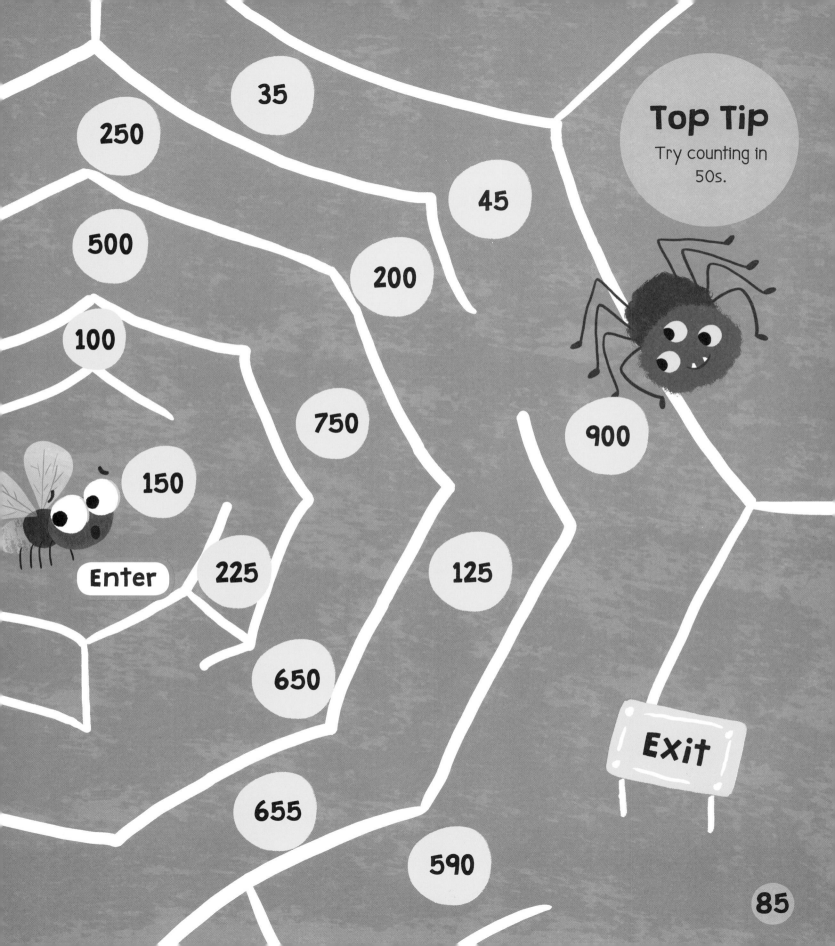

35

250

Top Tip
Try counting in 50s.

45

500

200

100

750

900

150

225

125

Enter

650

Exit

655

590

85

Divide by 50

Help the girl get to school as quickly as possible, but watch out for the puddles. Solve the calculations and follow the correct answers.

100÷50

10

5

12

1

2

50÷50

200÷50

600÷50

20

250÷50

3

13

3

150÷50

4

Start

Multiples of 25

Follow the numbers that are multiples of 25 to guide the safari truck back to the lodge.

Start

55

25

355

50

75

100

255

65

LODGE

125

135

155

175

Finish

Top Tip

Try counting in 25s.

150

ANSWERS

4–5 Doubles

6–7 Multiples of 2

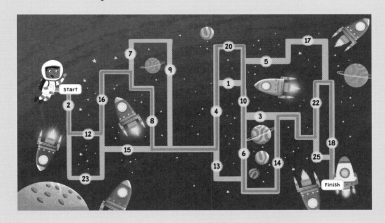

8–9 More multiples of 2

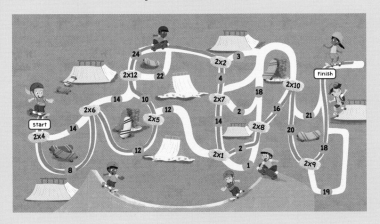

10–11 Divide by 2

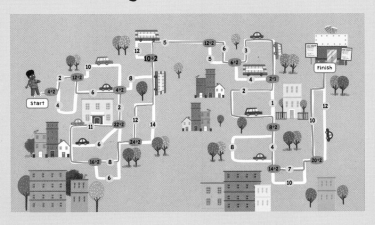

12–13 Multiples of 10

14–15 More multiples of 10

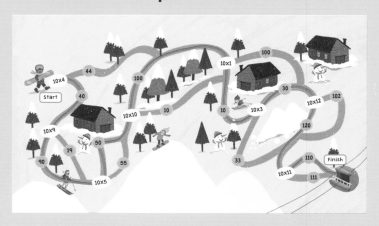

16–17 Divide by 10

18–19 Multiples of 5

20–21 More multiples of 5

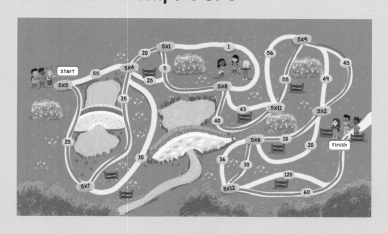

22–23 Divide by 5

24–25 Mixed multiples 2, 5, and 10.

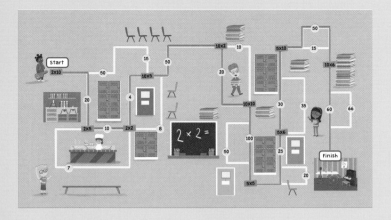

26–27 Mixed division 2, 5, and 10

28–29 Multiples of 4

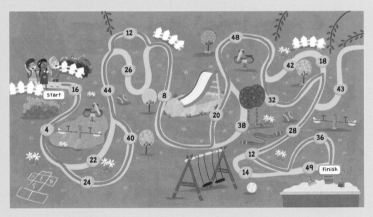

30–31 More multiples of 4

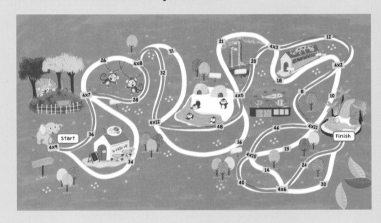

32–33 Divide by 4

34–35 Multiples of 8

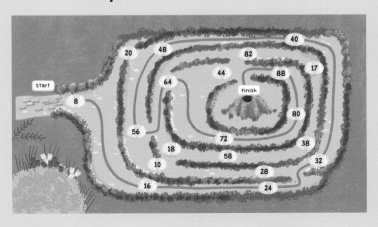

36–37 More multiples of 8

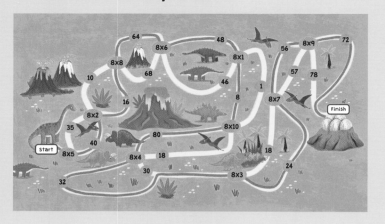

38–39 Divide by 8

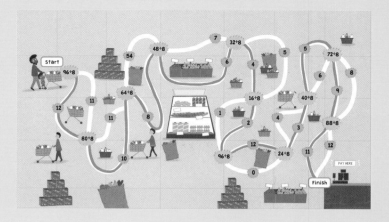

40–41 Mixed multiples 2, 4, and 8

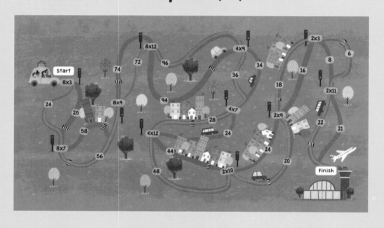

42–43 Mixed division 2, 4, and 8

44–45 Multiples of 3

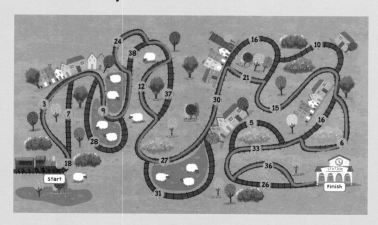

46–47 More multiples of 3

48–49 Divide by 3

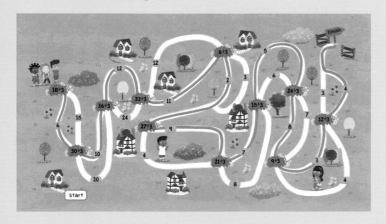

50–51 Multiples of 6

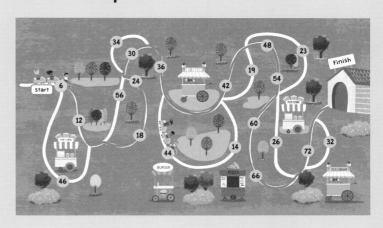

52–53 More multiples of 6

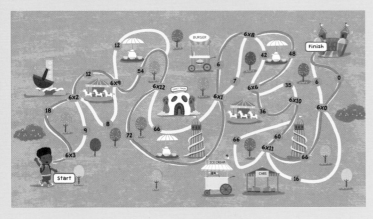

54–55 Divide by 6

56–57 Multiples of 9

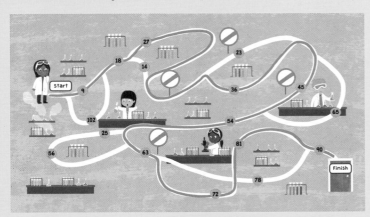

58–59 More multiples of 9

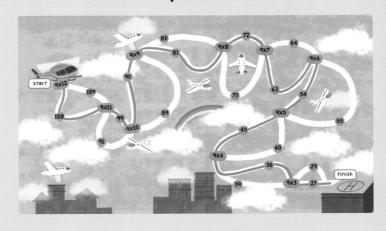

60-61 Divide by 9

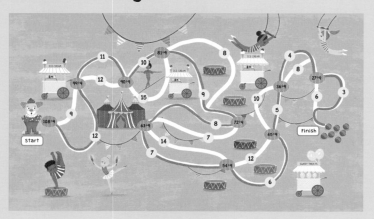

62-63 Mixed multiples of 3, 6, and 9

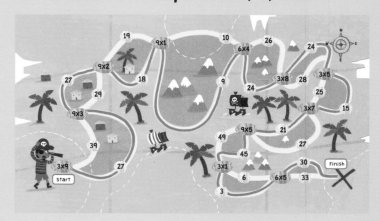

64-65 Divide and multiply 3, 6, and 9

66-67 Multiples of 11

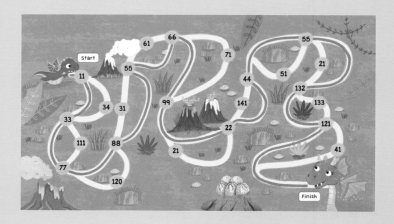

68-69 Divide by 11

70-71 Multiples of 12

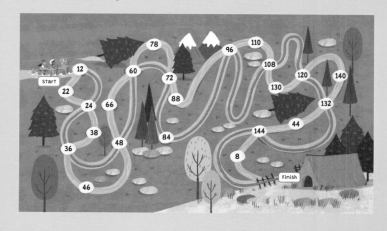

72–73 Divide by 12

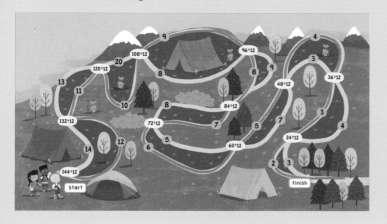

74–75 Mixed 10, 11, 12 multiplication

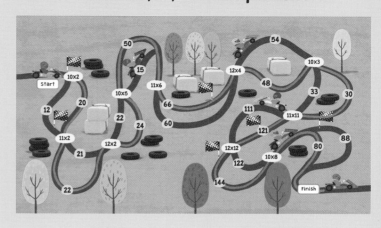

76–77 Mixed multiply and divide by 2

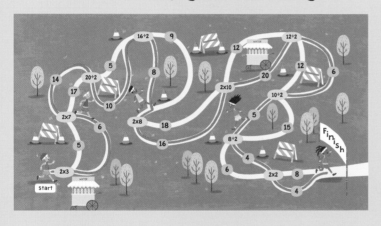

78–79 Mixed multiply and divide by 5

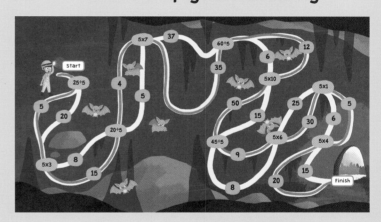

80–81 Multiples of 100

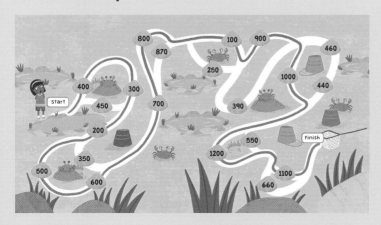

82–83 Divide by 100

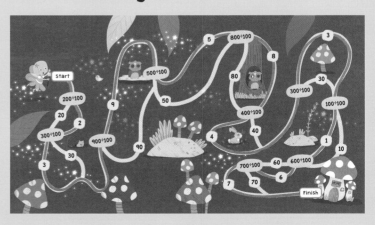

84–85 Multiples of 50

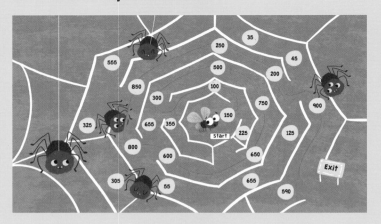

86–87 Divide by 50

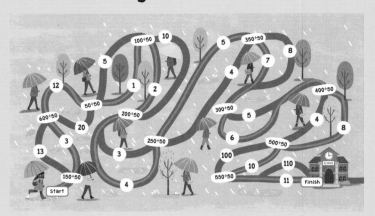

88 Multiples of 25

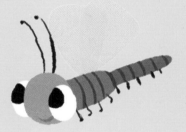